BUD, NOT BUDDY

By

REGINALD ANDRÉ JACKSON

Adapted from the novel

by

CHRISTOPHER PAUL CURTIS

Dramatic Publishing

Woodstock, Illinois • England • Australia • New Zealand

Printed in the United States of America

(BUD, NOT BUDDY)

ISBN: 978-1-58342-621-0

IMPORTANT BILLING AND CREDIT REQUIREMENTS

All producers of the play *must* give credit to Christopher Paul Curtis as author of the book and Reginald André Jackson as dramatizer of the play in all programs distributed in connection with performances of the play and in all instances in which the title of the play appears for purposes of advertising, publicizing or otherwise exploiting the play and/or a production. The names of Christopher Paul Curtis and Reginald André Jackson *must* also appear on a separate line, on which no other name appears, immediately following the title, and *must* appear in size of type not less than fifty percent (50%) the size of the title type. Biographical information on Christopher Paul Curtis and Reginald André Jackson, if included in the playbook, may be used in all programs. *In all programs this notice must appear:*

"Produced by special arrangement with
THE DRAMATIC PUBLISHING COMPANY of Woodstock, Illinois"

In addition, all producers of the play must include the following acknowledgment on the title page of all programs distributed in connection with performances of the play and on all advertising and promotional materials:

"First commissioned and developed in the 'Book-It Style™' by Book-It Repertory Theatre, founded in 1990, Seattle, Washington, www.book-it.org. Transforming great literature into great theatre through simple and sensitive production and inspiring audiences to read."

* * * *

A workshop of *Bud, Not Buddy* opened on January 14, 2006, at Book-It Repertory Theatre with the following cast:

Bud (not Buddy) . . . . *Earl Alexander*
Mr. Jimmy, Ensemble . . . . *L. Sterling Beard*
Herman E. Calloway . . . . *Frederick Charles Canada*
Librarian, Ensemble. . . . . *Margaret Philips Carter*
Momma, Ensemble . . . . *Rebecca M. Davis*
Bugs, Steady Eddie, Ensemble . . . . *Anthony Leroy Fuller*

Miss Thomas, Ensemble. . . . . *Demene E. Hall*
Lefty Lewis, Doo-Doo-Bug, Ensemble . . . . *Cecil Luellen*
Doug the Thug, Ensemble . . . . *Lance McQueen*
Deza Malone, Young Momma, Ensemble . . . *Shermona Mitchell*
Dirty Deed, Ensemble . . . . *Michael Place*

Director: Mark Jared Zufelt

Bud, Not Buddy received its world premiere on December 1, 2006, at Book-It Repertory Theatre in Seattle, Wash., with the following cast:

Bud (not Buddy). . . . . *Earl Alexander*
Mr. Jimmy, Ensemble . . . . *Bob Williams*
Herman E. Calloway . . . . *Bill Hall Jr.*
Librarian, Ensemble. . . . . *Natasha Sims*
Momma, Ensemble . . . . *Chelsea Binta*
Bugs, Steady Eddie, Ensemble . . . . *Brandon Boyd Simmons*
Miss Thomas, Ensemble. . . . . *Demene E. Hall*
Lefty Lewis, Doo-Doo-Bug, Ensemble . . . . *Cecil Luellen*
Billy, Toddy, Doug the Thug, Ensemble. . . . . *Stan Shields*
Deza Malone, Young Momma, Ensemble . . . *Shermona Mitchell*
Dirty Deed, Ensemble . . . . *John Ulman*

Director: Mark Jared Zufelt

Bud, Not Buddy opened on January 15, 2008, at the Children's Theatre Company, in Minneapolis, Minn., under the direction of Marion McClinton,

Approaching *Bud, Not Buddy*

This play has been written in the Book-It style. This allows the play to be supported by actual narrative from the novel. This narrative is most effective when treated as dialogue.

Example. Bud has the line.

The whole room smelled like eraser and it felt like something had poked the back of my eyeball.

Instead of staring out at the audience, a plausible way to deliver this line is to think:

Wow, this room smells like...like, is that eraser— Ow, ow, ow! What happened to my eye?

Bud, as our guide has several asides to the audience, as does the Announcer. Bugs speaks to the audience when he explains where his name comes from and when he's looking for the train. The entire ensemble addresses the audience as they become trees. Other than these moments the narrative is to be treated as in-the-moment dialogue, designed to keep the action moving (not to replace it).

Scenic Elements

I believe it is best to approach the staging of this play in much the same way Shakespeare tackled his plays.

"Think, when we talk of horses, that you see them,
Printing their proud hoofs i' the receiving earth;
For 'tis your thoughts that now must deck our kings,
Carry them here and there, jumping o'er times..."

There is no actual car. A hat stand can be a tree. Bud must visit several locations; many only once. A simplistic indication of place and time augmented by lights and sound is best. This allows scenes to dovetail on one another, eliminating cumbersome scene changes.

There are several opportunities for heightened theatricality, particularly in the first act. The more we can externalize Bud's imagination the better. In the second act, Bud's need to use his imagination for survival decreases dramatically. The few moments he has in that act, Herman as the Big Bad Wolf, recalling the lifeguard, can still be as large as the vampire in the first act.

Music note

The few lyrics used (bottom of page 82) are from "You'd Be So Nice to Come Home To." So as not to restrict any production for material that may not be in the public domain, I support a musical director's choice to substitute so long as the song reflects in some way a coming together or a coming home.

BUD, NOT BUDDY

CHARACTER ROLES

BUD, 10
BILLY, 12 or 13
BUGS, 10
CASEWORKER, 30s/40s
MOMMA, 26
JERRY, 6
BARKER, any age
YOUNG MR. CALLOWAY, 30s
MR. AMOS, 30s
MRS. AMOS, 30s
TODD AMOS, 12
ANNOUNCER, any age
VAMPIRE, any age
YOUNG MOMMA, 10
HORSE (nonspeaking), any age
LIBRARIAN, 30s/40s
DEZA'S DAD, 30s
DEZA'S MOM, 30s
DEZA, 11
JAKE, 30s
POLICE OFFICER, 30s
LEFTY, 40s/50s
COP, 30s
DOO-DOO-BUG, 30s
HERMAN E. CALLOWAY, 40s/50, (bald, big belly)
DIRTY DEED, 30s
DOUG THE THUG, 30s
JIMMY, 40s
STEADY EDDIE, 30s
MISS THOMAS, 30s/40s
TYLA, 20s/30s
LIFEGUARD, any age

POSSIBLE DOUBLING

Bud
Ensemble #1 . . . . Billy, Doug the Thug
Ensemble #2 . . . . Bugs, Young Mr. Calloway, Todd Amos, Steady Eddie
Ensemble #3 . . . . Caseworker, Mrs. Amos, Deza's Mom, Miss Thomas
Ensemble #4 . . . . Momma
Ensemble #5 . . . . Jerry, Deza's Dad, Jimmy

Ensemble #6. . . Barker, Mr. Amos, Horse, Lefty, Doo-Doo-Bug
Ensemble #7 . . . . *Announcer*, Vampire, Jake, Cop,
Dirty Deed, Lifeguard
Ensemble #8 . . . . Young Momma, Deza, Tyla
**Ensemble #9* . . . . Librarian, Police Officer
Ensemble #10. . . . . Herman E. Calloway

All actors save the ones playing Bud and Herman E. Calloway should be considered as cast. They play the breathers, animals and numbered characters.

All lines and characters should be distributed to suit the strengths of the production at hand. The doubling assignments above are just an example.

Ensemble #7: The roles of Jake, Cop and Dirty Deed should be portrayed by a white male.

**Announcer*: The Announcer lines can be divvied amongst the Ensemble or played by the same actor as Dirty Deed.

**Ensemble #9*: These roles can be played by a white female, or Ensemble #9 can be omitted. To do so one could have the white male play the Librarian and have a black male actor play Police Officer. The officer is just muscle for hire, employed by the Pinkertons. I have no idea whether a black actor in this role would confuse an audience, or if his subsequent resignation would be more effecting.

ACT ONE

Scene 1

(A group of boys attack the stage. Some play at marbles and jacks, others roughhouse. Standing in a pool of light we find BUD CALDWELL. He places his suitcase on the ground and opens it. He addresses the audience.)

BUD. Most kids in the home keep their things in a paper or cloth sack, but not me.

#1. Bud has his own suitcase.

BUD. Of treasures. *(Of five flyers, he takes out the only blue one. He regards it with great reverence.)* The paper's starting to wear out but I like checking to see if there's anything I hadn't noticed before.

BILLY. The boys at the home were getting their nightly teasing from the biggest bully there was.

ALL. Billy Burns.

BILLY. I don't even belong to this place and it ain't going to be long before my momma comes and gets me out.

BUGS. Billy, your momma must have a real bad rememory. Seems like since she was the one what dropped you off here she'd've remembered where she left you by now.

BILLY. Well, well, well, look at who piped up, Mr. Bugs. I wouldn't expect a little ignorant roach-head like you to know nothing about folks coming back here to get you out. Any fool you see walking down the street could be them. Seven little boys in this room and not a one of y'all knows who your folks is.

BUD. That's not true, I know who my momma is, I lived with her for six years.

BILLY. And what about your old man? How many years you live with him? I got a nickel here and you know what it says? *(BILLY holds the nickel up, moves it like a puppeteer and speaks in his best buffalo voice.)* Billy, my man, go ahead and bet this little no-momma fool he don't know who his daddy is, then I'd have another nickel to bang around in your pocket with.

BUD. You owe me a nickel, my daddy plays a giant fiddle and his name is Herman E. Calloway— *(The boys erupt in an explosion of laughter.)* And with those words that I didn't even mean to say a little seed of a idea started growing.

(A CASEWORKER enters. The whip has been cracked. Children form a line facing downstage. The WORKER deliberately walks the line.)

BUD. Uh-oh, here *we go again. (CASEWORKER stops.)* Shoot! She stopped at me.

CASEWORKER. Are you Buddy Caldwell?

(Lights up on MOMMA.)

MOMMA. Bud is your name and don't you ever let anyone call you anything outside that either. Especially don't you ever let anyone call you Buddy.

BUD. Yes, Momma.

MOMMA. Don't you worry. *(Lights out on MOMMA. She exits.)*

BUD. It's Bud, not Buddy, ma'am.

CASEWORKER *(grabs another child)*. Aren't you Jerry Clark? Boys, good news! You both have been accepted in new temporary-care homes starting this afternoon!

JERRY. Together?

CASEWORKER. Why, no. Jerry, you'll be in a family with three little girls…

BUD. Jerry looked like—

JERRY. He'd just found out they were going to dip him in a pot of boiling milk.

CASEWORKER. And Bud, you'll be with Mr. and Mrs. Amos and their son who's twelve years old. That makes him just two years older than you, doesn't it, Bud?

BUD. Yes, ma'am.

CASEWORKER. Now, now, boys, no need to look so glum. There's a depression going on, people can't find jobs and we've been lucky enough to find two wonderful families who've opened their doors for you. Gather your things. *(She exits.)*

BUD. Here *we go again*. This was the third foster home I was going to, but it still surprises me when my nose gets all runny and my throat gets all choky and my eyes get all sting-y. But the tears coming out doesn't happen.

JERRY. Jerry sat on his bed.

BUD. I could tell that he was losing the fight not to cry.

JERRY. Tears were popping out of his eyes and slipping down his cheeks.

BUD. I couldn't help but feel sorry for Jerry. Six is a real rough age to be at. Most folks think you start to be an adult when you're fifteen or sixteen years old, but it really starts when you're around six.

JERRY. It's around six that grown folks stop giving you little swats and taps and jump clean up to giving you slugs that'll have you seeing stars in the middle of the day.

BUD. The first foster home I was in taught me that real quick.

JERRY. They expect you to know everything they mean. It's around six that your teeth start coming a-loose in your mouth. Unless you're as stupid as a lamppost you've got to wonder what's coming off next, your arm? Your leg? Your neck? Every morning it seems a lot of your parts aren't stuck on as good as they use to be.

BUD. Three girls sounds terrible, Jerry, but the worst thing that's going to happen is that they're going to make you play house a lot. They'll probably make you be the baby and do this kind of junk to you. *(Tickles him.)* Ga-ga goo-goo, baby-waby. You're going to be great. *(BUD crosses downstage and addresses the audience.)* Six is real tough. That's how old I was when I knocked on Momma's bedroom door… *(Door opens. Sound of sirens. Flashing of lights.)* Then found her. *(BUD plops down on his suitcase and examines his blue flyer.)* Something was telling me there was a message for me on this flyer, but I didn't have the decoder ring.

(A man [BARKER] is revealed standing on a street corner passing out flyers. His face is obscured. As he speaks a spotlight appears; standing in it is YOUNG MR. CALLOWAY playing a bass.)

BARKER. Limited engagement. Direct from an S.R.O. engagement in New York City—Herman E. Calloway and the Dusky Devastators of the Depression!

YOUNG MR. CALLOWAY. In the middle of the flyer was a blurry picture of a man.

BUD. I've never met him, but I have a pretty good feeling that this guy must be my father. Underneath the picture someone had writ—

BARKER. One night only in Flint, Michigan, at the luxurious Fifty Grand on Saturday June 16th, 1932. Nine until—

(MOMMA enters and takes a flyer from the BARKER. She crosses in to BUD.)

BUD. I remember Momma bringing this flyer with her when she came from working one day.

MOMMA. She got very upset.

BUD. I couldn't understand, she kept four others that were a lot like it. *(BUD sits struggling to decode the flyer.)*

MOMMA. But this one got her really jumpy. *(Exits.)*

(Lights shift.)

BUD. The only difference I could see was that the others didn't say anything about Flint on them.

(Lights shift as we are introduced to the AMOSES. MR. and MRS. and TODD AMOS stand next to a bed. MRS. AMOS waves BUD over. He turns back to the audience and speaks.)

BUD. Here we go again. *(BUD crosses to the bed and climbs in. The AMOSES exit turning out the light.)*

Scene 2

(TODD AMOS re-enters BUD's new room. He is carrying a long yellow pencil. He stops at BUD's head and bends over his face. BUD squirms. TODD turns facing downstage holding the pencil like a thermometer. He wears a robe, slippers and a gigantic smile.)

BUD. It felt like a steam locomotive had jumped the tracks and chug-chug-chugged its way straight into my nose.

TODD. Wow! You got all the way up to R! *(TODD shows BUD the writing on his pencil.)*

BUD. Ticonderoga? The whole room smelled like eraser and it felt like something had poked the back of my eyeball.

TODD. I've never gotten it in as deep as the N on any of you other little street urchins. I just might enjoy your stay here, Buddy?

BUD. I wasn't about to let anybody call me Buddy and stick a pencil up my nose.

TODD. All the way to the R.

BUD. My fist came open and when it landed it made a pop like a .22 rifle going off.

(A huge smile appears on TODD's face as he slowly undoes his robe and lets it fall to the ground. BUD throws himself off the bed fists up, as we hear the opening bell to a title fight. They dance around each other.)

BUD. He could kiss my wrist if he thought I was going to let him whip me up without a good fight. Being this brave. *(TODD punches him square on the nose.)*

TODD. Was kind of stupid. *(TODD proceeds to whip BUD up without a good fight.)* Even though Todd— *(Punch.)*

BUD. Was a puffy, rich old mama's boy— *(BUD ducks)* who wore a robe and slippers.

TODD. He could hit like a mule. *(Punch. BUD drops to the floor in a ball.)*

BUD. There comes a time when you're losing a fight that it just doesn't make sense to keep fighting. It's not that you're being a quitter, it's just that you've got the sense to know when enough is enough.

(MRS. AMOS enters. TODD kicks BUD repeatedly. Upon seeing his mom, he falls to his knees, and grabs his throat. He begins to wheeze heavily.)

MRS. AMOS. Toddy? Toddy boy? You little cur, what have you done to Toddy?

TODD *(breath labored)*. Oh, Mother…I was only trying to help…and…and look what it's gotten me. *(TODD points to his cheek.)*

MRS. AMOS. How dare you! Not only have you struck him, you have provoked his asthma!

TODD. I just tried to waken him to make sure he'd gone to the lavatory, Mother. Look at him, this one's got "bed-wetter" written all over him.

MRS. AMOS. Mrs. Amos hated bed-wetters more than anything in the world.

BUD. I'm not bragging when I say that I'm one of the best liars in the world; Todd was pretty doggone good. He knew some of the same rules and things I know. Shucks, I've got so many of them rememorized that I had to give them numbers, and it seemed like Todd knew number 3 of…

(Fanfare.)

ANNOUNCER. Bud Caldwell's Rules and Things for Having a Funner Life and Making a Better Liar Out of Yourself. Rules and Things Number 3—

BUD. **If you got to tell a lie, make sure it's simple and easy to remember.**

TODD. Todd had done that.

MRS. AMOS. You beastly little brute, I will not tolerate even one night of you under my roof.

(MR. AMOS enters.)

MRS. AMOS. Lord knows I have been stung by my own people before. I do not have time to put up with the foolishness of those members of our race who do not want to be uplifted. In the morning I'll be getting in touch with the home and, much as a bad penny, you shall return to them. Mr. Amos will show you to the shed. *(BUD reaches for his suitcase.)* Oh, no, we shall hold on to his beloved valuables. Apologize or I shall be forced to give you the strapping of your life. *(MRS. AMOS raises her hand. She is holding a belt.)*

BUD. I'd apologize. One beating from these Amoses was enough for me.

MRS. AMOS. Well?

BUD. I started shooting apologies out.

TODD. Like John Dillinger shoots out bullets.

BUD. It was wrong to hit you. I know you were only trying to help. *(To MR. AMOS.)* And sir, I'm sorry I got you out of your sleep.

(MRS. AMOS begins swatting the inside of her palm with the belt.)

MRS. AMOS. Mrs. Amos?

BUD. Was going to be the hardest— I'm so grateful for all of your help. And I'm really, really sorry… I could see—

MRS. AMOS. She needed more.

BUD. Please don't send me back— I was being just like Brer Rabbit, when he yelled out, "Please, Brer Fox, don't throw me in the pricker patch." This was…

(Fanfare.)

ANNOUNCER. Bud Caldwell's Rules and Things to Make a Better Liar of Yourself. Number 118—

BUD. **You have to give adults something that they think they can use to hurt you by taking it away. That way they might not take something away that you really do want.**

MRS. AMOS. Enough. Put him in the shed. *(MRS. AMOS exits.)*

(MR. AMOS leaves to fetch BUD's linen. TODD's asthma vanishes.)

TODD. Buddy, keep a sharp eye out for the vampire bats. Oh, and watch out for those spiders and centipedes, Buddy.

BUD. I remember what happened to my best friend, Bugs.

(Lights up on BUGS. He is lying down, tugging, picking and fussing at his ear.)

BUGS. When a cockroach crawled in his ear one night at the home!

(ENSEMBLE MEMBERS 1, 3 and 4 converge on BUGS.)

#4. Four grown folks had held Bugs down—

#1. Whilst they tried to pull it out with a pair of tweezers.

#3. But the only thing that that did was pull the roaches back legs off. *(BUGS screams.)*

BUD. You'd have thought they were pulling his legs off, not some cockroach's!!

#3. They were going to have to take him to the emergency room to get the roach out.

(Shift. 1, 3 and 4 exit. BUGS steps toward BUD.)

BUD. It was almost morning when Bugs got back. Did they get it out?

BUGS. Oh, hi, Bud. Yeah, they got him.

BUD. Did it hurt a lot?

BUGS. Nope.

BUD. Were you scared?

BUGS. Nope.

BUD. Then how come you were screaming so doggone loud?

BUGS. I didn't know I was, I probably couldn't hear me screaming 'cause that roach was so loud.

BUD. I've seen lots of roaches but I've never heard one of them make any sound.

BUGS. Well, bugs ain't so different from us as you'd think; soon as he saw those tweezers coming he commenced to screaming, screaming in English too, not some bug language like you'd expect from a roach.

BUD. Yeah? What'd he say?

BUGS. All he kept yelling was, "My legs! My legs! Why have they done this to my legs?" *(BUGS faces the audience.)* That's the true story about how Bugs started getting called Bugs. *(BUGS bows and exits.)*

(BUD looks at TODD. MR. AMOS grabs BUD by the arm.)

TODD. The last kid who got put in there got stung so bad he was swole up as big as a whale. The kid before that hasn't been found to this day. All that's left is that big puddle of his blood on the floor.

(MR. AMOS guides BUD toward the kitchen door. BUD stops in his tracks.)

BUD. There was a double-barreled shotgun leaning against the side of the icebox. *(BUD spies his suitcase. He reaches for it. MR. AMOS pulls him back.)* My suitcase! *(MR. AMOS drags BUD the rest of the way outside.)*

MR. AMOS. Into the dark. *(MR. AMOS hands BUD the blanket and pillow and nudges BUD inside.)*

BUD. If I was like a normal kid I would've bust out crying. There was a big black stain in the dirt! They really were going to make me sleep in a shed with a patch of blood from that kid who had disappeared out of here a couple weeks ago!

Scene 3

(Five members of the ENSEMBLE join BUD in the dark. They are all breathing heavily and sometimes echo BUD's words.)

BUD. The only thing I could hear was my own breath.

#1. It sounded like there were six scared people locked up in the shed.

BUD. I thought real hard about making my breathing slowww dowwwn.

#2 *(sotto voce)*. Pretty soon it sounded like—

BUD. The five other breathers had left. I reached my hand toward the doorknob and went from kind of calm *(BREATHERS converge on BUD, panting throughout)* to being in that—

BREATHERS. Stand-in-one-place-with-spit-drooling-down-the-front-of-your-shirt—

BUD. Kind of scared.

#1. Halfway up the door were three little flat monster heads guarding the doorknob.

#3. Each head had two little round eyes—

#4. And a wide-open mouth with a sharp set of pointy teeth ready to bite.

#1. The doorknob guards were three dried-out fish heads that someone had nailed to the door.

(BUD pokes at a pile of rags with his shoe. He takes a rag and places it over the fish heads. The panting stops.)

BUD. So, I can't see you and you can't see me… What was the best way to sleep?

#1. I'd bet a thousand dollars that there were roaches on the floor of this shed, just waiting to crawl in someone's ear.

(BUD spreads the blanket on the woodpile. Fighting his fear he tries to sleep.)

BUD. When I blinked my eyes open, I wished I'd stayed asleep. *(The breathing resumes.)* Up at the very top of the shed was.

VAMPIRE. The biggest vampire bat you'd ever see!

BUD. I wasn't about to let this vampire suck my blood dry without a war; he could kiss my wrist if he thought that was going to happen. *(He picks up a rake and holds it like a Louisville Slugger.)* I eyed where the bat was sleeping and revved the rake like I was going to hit a four-hundred-foot home run.

(Fanfare.)

ANNOUNCER. Bud Caldwell's Rules for Having a Funner Life Number 328.

BUD. **When you make up your mind to do something, hurry up and do it. If you wait you might talk yourself out of what you wanted in the first place...** Shucks, I couldn't remember for sure if you killed a vampire by…

#1. Driving a stake through its heart.

#4. Shooting it with a silver bullet.

BUD. If I was wrong I was—

VAMPIRE. Going to be trapped in the shed with a vampire who was going to be real upset that someone had woke him up by whacking him with a rake.

BUD. I closed my eyes and swung it like I was Paul Bunyan chopping down a tree with one blow. I opened my eyes just in time to see the vampire—

ALL. Get cut right in half. *(The VAMPIRE crumples to the ground.)*

BUD. I was kind of surprised it didn't scream or cry or say—

VAMPIRE. Curses, you got me!

BUD. The next sound I heard was even worse than if the vampire had said—

VAMPIRE *(rising)*. Aha, you doggone kid, that hurt, but now I get my revenge! *(A big hum of buzzing is heard. BUD grabs his face. He screams. Pulling his arm away he unclenches his fist, revealing a wasp. He tries to squeeze the life out of it, but is stung in the hand. He screams.)* What I'd thought was a vampire bat hanging on the ceiling was really—

ALL. A hornets' nest.

#4. And now there were about six thousand hornets flying around in the tiny shed.

BUD. And each and every one of them was looking for me. *(BUD suffers multiple stings.)* I charged at the door like Paul Robeson running down the football field. *(He charges, connects, screams and retreats.)*

#3. This wasn't a real good idea.

BUD. I forgot all about the fish-head door guards. Little needle teeth cut me like a razor. *(He tries the window again. It opens. He is stung repeatedly. But manages to squeeze through the window. He swats at himself until all hornets are dead.)* I wondered how hard I'd have to pull the trigger on that double-barreled shotgun for it to go off. *(BUD crawls through the Amos' kitchen window.)* Aha, you doggone Amoses, that hurt, but now I get my revenge.

Scene 4

(#s 1, 3 and 4 follow BUD through the window. Inside, BUD spies out his suitcase. He and his followers whisper throughout.)

BUD. My suitcase. Whew, it was the right weight.

#4. The shotgun was still there.

#1. Fair is fair.

#4. The Amoses deserved what they were going to get.

BUD. My heart started jumping around in my stomach. I could smell the gun oil. *(BUD aims the gun and mimes shooting animals.)* Elephant. Dragon. Tiger. Todd!

#4. Imagine how it would feel to creep up to his bed while he was sleeping and put the shotgun barrel right in his nose.

BUD. Too dangerous. The first part of my revenge plan was to get this gun out of the way. *(He hides the gun.)* I felt a lot better when it was out of my hands. I started opening cupboards. *(He finds a jelly jar and turns on the hot water spigot.)*

#1. These Amoses had hot water running right into the house.

BUD. I stuck a jelly jar underneath until it was filled to the brim.

#1. Todd's door came open easy as anything.

(Lights up on TODD asleep. BUD approaches the bed.)

#4 *(sleep talking)*. He was deep asleep. *(He grabs TODD by the hand and sticks his fingers in the jar.)*

BUD. One of the older boys at the home told me if you dipped someone's hand in a warm glass of water whilst they're asleep they don't have any choice but to pee the bed. It's something about chemistry and biology making some valve in your guts open up and…woop, zoop, sloop…you got a wet bed. *(He studies TODD expectantly. Fusses with his fingers in the jar, and waits.)* Todd's bed stayed dry as the desert. *(#s 1 and 4 gesture for BUD to pour water on TODD's pjs. He does. TODD's face twitches a couple of times. He smiles.)*

#4. The warm water opened that little valve up and…

TODD. Woop, zoop, sloop…

#1. He soaked his sheets!

BUD. He who laughs last laughs best. Ha-ha-ha. *(BUD grabs his suitcase and exits the AMOSES.)* Man! I was on the lam. If J. Edgar Hoover and the FBI saw me now I'd be in some real serious hot water.

Scene 5

BUD. Being on the lam was a whole lot of fun…for about five minutes. I can tell a nervous-looking, stung-up kid with blood dripping from a fish-head bite and carrying a old raggedy suitcase doesn't belonged around here. I can slip through the windows of the library, in the morning Miss Hill could help me.

(As lights come up we find a few fir trees and a closed door. He creeps up to the door and peeks in the window. Then sneaks around back. BUD starts to break down crying but holds it together.)

BUD. Somebody had gone and put big metal bars on the windows. *(Crossing back around front he slides under the trees, and he opens his suitcase.)* Most folks don't have sense enough to carry a blanket around with them, but you never know when you might be sleeping under a Christmas tree at the library. They had been fumbling through my treasures. My rocks. *(He counts the rocks. He is pleased with his count. He fishes out an envelope. He opens it.)* This was the only picture of Momma in the world.

(MOMMA enters. As she speaks lights come up on YOUNG MOMMA and HORSE.)

MOMMA. Running across the top of it was a sign, it said, boys and girls of Grand Rapids—follow the gentle light to the Miss B. Gotten Moon Park. Underneath the sign, between two wagon wheels—

YOUNG MOMMA. Was Momma.

BUD. She was about as old as I am now. I can't understand why she was so unhappy.

YOUNG MOMMA. Momma was sitting on a real live little midget horse. *(HORSE whinnies.)*

BUD. She had two six-shooter pistols in her hands—

YOUNG MOMMA. And she wished she could've emptied them on somebody.

BUD. And I know who.

MOMMA. Her father.

BUD. My granddad.

YOUNG MOMMA. He'd gone and ruined everybody's fun that day by getting in a big fight with me about the gigantic white twenty-five-gallon Texas cowboy hat I was wearing.

MOMMA. That hardheaded man insisted that I wear that horrible hat.

BUD. Momma wasn't looking like she had rocks in her jaw because the hat was so fake.

YOUNG MOMMA. She was mad because the hat was so dirty.

(MOMMA searches around and makes quick manic movements throughout her tirade.)

MOMMA. Filth! Absolute filth! *(She gets up, storms over to YOUNG MOMMA, rips the hat off her head and shoos YOUNG MOMMA and HORSE off stage. MOMMA then tosses the hat off after them.)* I'm sure it was crawling with ringworm, lice and tetters! Do you imagine it ever occurred to him to wash it?

BUD. No, Momma.

MOMMA. But your grandfather insisted, insisted mind you…

BUD. Yes, Momma… She was like a tornado. *(She stops and grabs BUD by the arms.)* The only time stuff didn't blow around was when she'd squeeze my arms and tell me things over and over and over and over. She had favorites.

MOMMA. Bud is your name and don't you ever let anyone call you anything outside of that either. I may have some problems but being stupid isn't one of them, I would've added that "dy" onto the end of your name if I intended for it to be there. Buddy is a dog's name or a name that someone's going to use on you if they're being false-friendly. Your name is Bud, period.

BUD. I'd say, OK, Momma. And she'd say, every single time—

MOMMA. And do you know what a bud is?

BUD. I always answered, yes, Momma, but it was like she didn't hear me.

MOMMA. A bud is a flower-to-be. Waiting for just the right care and warmth to open up. It's a little fist of love waiting to unfold and be seen by the world. And that's you.

BUD. I know she didn't mean anything by naming me after a flower, but it's sure not something I tell anybody about.

MOMMA. Don't you worry, Bud.

BUD. That didn't make me calm at all. That was…

(Fanfare.)

ANNOUNCER. Bud Caldwell's Rules and Things to Have a Funner Life Number 83.

BUD. **If a adult tells you not to worry, and you weren't worried before, you better hurry up and start 'cause you're already running late.**

(MOMMA grabs his arms and looks hard in his face. She will not be with him for long.)

MOMMA. And Bud, no matter how bad things look to you, no matter how dark the night, when one door closes, don't worry, because another door opens. *(Exits.)*

BUD. That was the thing that was supposed to help me. I couldn't see what one door closing had to do with another one opening unless there was a ghost involved. All her talk made me start jamming a chair up against my closet door at night. But now that I'm ten years old and just about a man I see Momma meant doors like the door at the home closing leading to the door at the Amoses opening and the door in the shed opening leading to me sleeping under a tree getting ready to open the next door.

(There is a shift. A glimmer of light appears on the library door as BUD falls asleep. Lights shift and sounds of morning arise. He wakes approaches the door and enters.)

Scene 6

(ENSEMBLE MEMBERS are dispersed about the library. Some are reading with stacks around them, some searching the aisles. A LIBRARIAN is restocking the shelves. They all speak in tones of reverence for the library.)

BUD. The air in the library isn't like the air anywhere else. *(He takes a book.)*

#7. You could sniff that soft, powdery, drowsy smell that comes off the pages in little puffs.

BUD *(doing all he can to stay awake)*. I think it's that smell that makes so many folks fall asleep in the library.

#4. You can imagine a puff of page powder coming up really slow and easy until it starts piling on the person's eyelashes.

#7 *(referring to #3)*. Their heads start bouncing up and down.

#3. Like they're bobbing in a big tub of water for apples, and before you know it… Woop. *(#3's head goes crashing down onto the page.)*

#4. Zoop.

BUD. Sloop. *(BUD's head goes crashing onto a page.)*

#7. Their face thunks down smack-dab on the book.

LIBRARIAN. That's the part that gets the librarians the maddest. *(She pulls #3's head from the book.)* They get real upset if folks start drooling in the books.

#3. Page powder—

LIBRARIAN. They don't want to hear no excuses, you gotta get out. *(#3 exits.)*

#7 *(waking BUD)*. Drooling in the books is even worse than laughing out loud in the library.

LIBRARIAN *(dabs at the drool from #3's book)*. There's nothing worse than opening a book and having the pages all stuck together from somebody's dried-up slobber.

BUD. Ma'am, I'm looking for Miss Hill.

LIBRARIAN. Miss Hill. My goodness, hadn't you heard?

BUD. Uh-oh! That's one of the worst. That's…

(Fanfare.)

ANNOUNCER *(sotto voce)*. Bud Caldwell's Rules and Things for Having a Funner Life Number 16.

BUD. **If a grownup ever starts a sentence by saying, "Haven't you heard?" get ready, 'cause what's about to come out of their mouth is gonna drop you head-first into a boiling tragedy.**

#4. "Haven't you heard?" always has something to do with someone kicking the bucket.

#7. It's usually something like hearing that your grand-mother got her whole body pulled through the wringer on a washing machine.

LIBRARIAN. There's no need for you to look so stricken, unless you had matrimonial plans concerning Miss Hill.

BUD. No, ma'am, I didn't plan that at all.

LIBRARIAN. Good, because I don't think her new hus-band would appreciate the competition. Charlemae… Miss Hill is currently living in Chicago, Illinois. It's not that far; here I'll show you.

BUD. It was a big map of Michigan and a couple of states next to it.

LIBRARIAN. We're here. And Chicago is here in Illinois.

BUD. How long would it take someone to walk that far?

LIBRARIAN. Oh, quite a while. Let's check the distance. *Standard Highway Mileage Guide.*

BUD. She showed me how to—

LIBRARIAN. Find Chicago on the line that was running across the page and…

BUD. Flint on the line that was running down the page?

LIBRARIAN. And then to look up the number that was writ where the two of them joined up.

BUD. 270.

LIBRARIAN. OK, this is how one figures the amount of time required to walk to Chicago. Now— *(She reaches for a third book.)*

BUD. Librarians. I asked one question and already she has us digging through three different books.

LIBRARIAN. Aha, the average male human gait is five miles an hour. All we have to do is divide two hundred seventy by five. *(She does so.)* Fifty-four hours! No, I'm afraid you'll simply have to wait until Mrs. Rollins comes back.

BUD. Shucks. Miss Hill might as well be a squashed, crunched-up mess in a washing machine. I walked into the regular air and stinking smells of Flint. That library door closing was the exact kind of door Momma had told me about. Since it had closed the next one was about to open. *(BUD climbs under his blanket and sleeps.)*

Scene 7

(Shift. A figure hovers over BUD. The figure steps on a stick. BUD's blanket tenses.)

BUD. My eyes snapped open and I was wide awake. I kept as still as I could. Whatever it was, knew I'd woked up—

BUGS. 'Cause it kept as still as it could too.

BUD. I got my fingers wrapped around my jackknife.

(The figure jumps on BUD trapping him under the blanket. They struggle.)

BUGS. Trapped as a roach under a dishrag! If you ain't a kid called Bud from the home I'm really sorry about jumping on you like this!

BUD. Bugs! Doggone it, Bugs, it is me! You nearly scared me to death!

BUGS *(helps BUD up)*. I'm sorry, Bud, but everybody knows how you like to sleep with that knife open so I figured I'd best grab holt of you so's you wouldn't wake up slicing nobody.

BUD. How come you aren't back at the home? You're on the lam.

BUGS. Yup, I'm going back to riding the rails. When I heard about you beating that kid up so bad that you had to take off I figured it was time for me to get going too. I thought you might be hanging around the library. Want to go with me?

BUD. Where you heading?

BUGS. Fruits to be picked out West. Did you really beat a kid up who was two years older than you?

BUD. Uh-huh, we kind of had a fight. Will we be sleeping on the train and everything?

BUGS. Sure. Some of the time the train don't stop for two or three days. Man, I always try to tell people that just because someone's skinny it don't mean they can't fight. You're a hero now, Bud!

BUD. Naw. How we going to use the toilet if the train doesn't stop?

BUGS. You just kind of lean out of the door and go. You get a real nice breeze.

BUD. Oh, man! Count me in!

BUGS. We got our slobs mixed up real good. *(BUGS spits into the palm of his hand. BUD spits into the palm of his hand. They slap hands hard.)*

BUD. Now it was official, I finally had a brother!

BUGS. We'll go down to the mission. There's bound to be someone there that knows about where we can hop this train, then we'll be on the lam together.

Scene 8

(Shift. BUGS turns to the audience and asks—)

BUGS. Anybody know where we can hop this train? *(Audience reacts. He returns to BUD.)* Have to go to a city called Hooperville.

(As they travel they question more people who simply shrug, and walk on.)

#6. Hooperville? Hooperville? *(#6 shakes his head and exits. They travel.)*

BUGS. I never heard of a city that was so doggone hard to find.

(The sky darkens as they meet #5 who points out directions.)

#5 *(laughing)*. Hooperville? Walk on the trail through the woods that run right up against Thread Crick. *(#5 exits. The sound of a harmonica is heard and signs of a fire are seen in the sky.)*

BUD. Smell the food cooking.

(A large group of people appear around a fire. Other ENSEMBLE MEMBERS stand or squat in smaller clusters about the stage.)

BUGS. We started cutting through the trees. That way we could peek into Hooperville first.

BUD. Right near our tree was a big fire with a pot that was big enough to bury a whole person in it.

(An ENSEMBLE MEMBER stirs the pot, pulls out some wet clothes and hands them to another who hangs them. A baby cries.)

BUGS. There were five white people sitting at a real small fire, off to the side by itself.

BUD. The baby sounded like all those new sick babies at the home. We can't just go busting into this city and expect someone to feed us, can we?

BUGS. One of us has got to talk to them; let's flip for it.
BUD. OK.
BUGS *(rubs a coin against his pants)*. Heads I win, tails you lose.
BUD. OK.

(BUGS flips the coin, catches it and slaps it down on the back of his hand. He takes a peek and smiles.)

BUGS. Tails. You lose.
BUD. Dang! So what should I say?
BUGS. Ask them if this is Hooperville; see if they got any extra food.

(BUD approaches the group.)

BUD. Excuse me, is this here Hooperville? *(Everyone laughs.)*
DEZA'S DAD. Naw, son, what you're looking for is Hooverville, sir. With a v, like in President Herbert Hoover.
BUD. Oh, is this it, sir?
DEZA'S DAD. This is one of them. Mr. Hoover worked so hard at making sure every city has got one that it seems like it would be criminal to call them anything else.

(Crowd cries, "Amen, brother," "That's the truth." BUGS crosses in.)

BUGS. What if we was looking for the Hooverville in Detroit or Chicago, how could this be the right one to be in?

DEZA'S DAD *(waves his mouth organ like a magic wand)*. Boys, look around you.

BUD. The raggedy little huts were in every direction you looked.

BUGS. People were all the colors you could think of, black, white and brown.

BUD. The fire made everyone look like they were different shades of orange.

BUGS. There were dark orange folks sitting next to medium orange folks sitting next to light orange folks.

DEZA'S DAD. All these people are just like you. Hungry and scared. Any place there're other folks in need of the same things that you are is the right place to be. The road ain't fit for a dog, much less a couple of kids. This is the right Hooverville for you.

DEZA'S MOM. Say, why don't we feed these boys?

DEZA'S DAD. We all pitch in here, so's unless either one of you is carrying one of them smoked West Virginny hams in them bags, it looks like you'll be pulling KP tonight.

DEZA'S MOM. That, m'lords, is your china. Please be careful not to chip it. You're lucky, it's muskrat stew tonight. *(She hands the boys sardine tins. The begin to eat.)*

BUD. Pulling what, sir?

DEZA'S DAD. Kitchen Police; you do the cleanup. There's a couple of other young folks who'll show you what you have to do.

BUGS/BUD. Yes, sir!

BUD. It tasted great.

DEZA'S MOM. You boys leave your bags here, it's time to do the dishes now. *(She waves DEZA over and reaches for BUD's suitcase.)*

BUD. Uh-oh. Ma'am, I like to keep my suitcase with me wherever I go.

DEZA'S MOM. I promise you your suitcase will be safe here.

BUD. The Amoses had promised the same thing.

DEZA'S MOM. Son, we don't have no thieving in here, we all look out for each other.

BUD. Thank you, ma'am.

(DEZA and #6 bring crates of dishes over. As they travel the rising sound of the creek is heard.)

DEZA. I don't suppose neither one of you new boys knows how to do dishes the right way, do you?

BUGS. Dang, girl, you act like this is the first cardboard jungle I've been in; I know how you do dishes out here.

DEZA. OK then, you and you can do half, and me and this boy can do the others. What's your name?

BUD. Bud, not Buddy.

DEZA. I'm Deza Malone. You dry. So, you and your friend come down here to get on that train tomorrow?

BUD. Yup. You going to take the train too?

DEZA. Uh-uh. My daddy is. She was real fast at washing the dishes.

BUD. But she got kind of slow and was touching my hand a lot when it came to giving them to me.

DEZA. Where's your momma and daddy?

BUD. My mother died four years ago.

DEZA. Sorry to hear that.

BUD. It's OK. She died so quick and painless that she didn't even have time to close her eyes. She didn't even have time to make a face like she was hurting.

DEZA. So where's your daddy?

BUD. I think he lives in Grand Rapids; I never met him.

DEZA. Sorry to hear that. *(She grips him by the hand.)*

BUD. Shucks, she held right on to my hand when she said that. *(BUD frees himself from her.)* That's OK too.

DEZA. No, it's not, and you should quit pretending that it is.

BUD. Who said I'm pretending anything?

DEZA. My momma says these poor kids on the road all alone are like dust in the wind. But I guess you're different. I guess you sort of carry your family around inside of you, huh?

BUD. I guess I do. Inside my suitcase, too.

DEZA. So you been staying in an orphanage since your momma died?

BUD. What makes you say that?

DEZA. I can tell by the way you act that you haven't been out on the road for very long. You still look young.

BUD. Shucks, I'm not all that young. Some folks think I'm a hero. *(DEZA laughs.)* A little dimple jumped up in her brown cheek.

DEZA. You ever kiss a girl at the orphanage?

BUD. Uh-oh! Are you kidding?

DEZA. No. Why, you afraid of girls?

BUD. You must be kidding.

DEZA. OK. *(She closes her eyes and mooshes her lips up and leans close to BUD.)*

BUD. Dangee! If I didn't kiss her she'd think I was scared of girls; if I did kiss her she might blab or Bugs might see. *(He looks down the creek to where BUGS is.)* It was dark enough. *(He kisses her and pulls back. She grabs him.)*

DEZA. We stuck like that for a hot second. *(She plants a big one on him. He opens his eyes. She smiles, eyes closed. She takes his hand. He looks at it and keeps his there. Somewhere a harmonica is heard. She gazes across the creek.)* Isn't this romantic?

BUD. The only thing I could see was the moon like a big egg yolk way up in the sky. I sneaked another peek at Deza's dimple.

DEZA. That's "Shenandoah" she's singing. Isn't it pretty?

BUD. I guess so.

DEZA. Listen.

(Singing is heard in the distance.)

DEZA'S MOM.

"It's been seven long years
Since last I've seen her,
Way hey, you rolling river,
Been seven long years,
Since last I've seen her,
Way hey, I'm bound away,
'Cross the wide Miss-oo-ray."

BUD *(with no love for what he's heard)*. Yup, that's a sad song.

DEZA. It's about an Indian man and woman who can't see each other for seven years. But in all that time they still stay in love. It reminds me of my mother and father.

BUD. Your dad's been gone for seven years before?

DEZA. She looked out over the crick.

BUD. The big eggy moon had her hypnotized. *(He looks at her then removes his hand.)* Well, that's just about it for the dishes.

DEZA. Bud, I'll never forget this night. *(They move toward BUGS.)*

BUD. I'd practiced on the back of my hand before, but this was the first time I'd ever busted slob with a real live girl.

BUGS. How come you're looking so strange, Bud? You look like you been chunked in the head with a rock.

(DEZA laughs. They arrive back at the main fire. DEZA'S MOM is there with BUD's suitcase. He takes it.)

BUD. Thank you very much, ma'am.

(BUGS leads BUD into a shanty.)

BUGS. We got in one of the shacks with some other boys. *(BUGS passes out, snoring loudly.)*

BUD. Deza's momma was right, someone who doesn't know who their family is, is like dust blowing around in a storm. I started wondering if going to California was the right thing to do. *(He goes through his suitcase, opens the pouch, pours out its contents.)* The rocks'd been in the drawer after the ambulance took Momma away. Someone had writ on all five of them, but it was writ in a code: "loogootee in. 5 dot 16 dot 11" "gary in. 6 dot 13 dot 12," "flint m. 8 dot 11 dot 11." *(Placing the rocks in the pouch he binds the string tight and drops it in the suitcase. He looks in envelope containing the Miss*

B. Gotten Moon Park photo. He places it back in the suitcase. He removes the flyers and counts them. He replaces them all save for the blue one, which he holds to the light.) Why'd this one bother Momma so much? This man just had to be my father. I used a little trick to help me fall off to sleep. I breathed in the smell real deep.

(He pulls the blanket over his head. We hear three deep breaths from under the blanket, and there is a shift. MOMMA appears behind BUD with a book.)

BUD.
After doing this three times the smells of the shack and Hooverville were gone. I took two more breaths and pretended I was hearing Momma reading to me about…

(MOMMA lists stories.)

MOMMA.
The Billy Goats Gruff, or the Fox and the Grapes, or the Dog That Saw His Reflection in the Water, or—

BUD.
Some other story she'd checked out of the library.

(MOMMA begins the story. BUD speaks over it.)

MOMMA.
Once upon a time there was a little red hen who lived in a big farmyard. She had three skinny yellow chicks. Now, one morning as they were busy scratching about the yard looking for something to eat, the little red hen found a grain of wheat.

BUD.
I imagined I was in the story until finally her voice and the story all mixed into one.

(BUD pauses to listen to the story.)

Look! She said. See what I found. Who will help me plant this grain of wheat? Not I, said the duck. I must be getting down to the pond to run some water thru these feathers. Not I, said the cat. I got company coming. I can't be getting my paws dirty. Very well, said the little red hen, I'll do it by my- self. Well, after time some weeds grew among the stalks of wheat. The little red hen asked: Who's going to help me pull these weeds? Not I, said the pig. I've got back problems. Not I, said the goat. I just got my beard done.

I'd learned that it was best to be asleep before Momma finished the story because if I was still awake she'd always tell me what the story was about. I never told Momma, but that always ruint the fun of the story.

Shucks, here I was thinking I was just hearing something funny about a fox or a dog and Momma spoilt it by telling me they were really lessons about not being greedy or not wishing for things you couldn't have. I heard…

Not I, said the big bad wolf…

(MOMMA watches his head drop as he falls asleep.)

MOMMA. Woop, zoop, sloop. No matter what happens I want you to sleep knowing that there has never been a little boy, anywhere, anytime, who was loved more than I love you.

(She kisses him and tiptoes away. As she exits, an empty spotlight appears to the thrumming sound of a bass. BUD jumps up, dreaming.)

BUD. Mr. Calloway? Herman E. Calloway? Dad?

(DEZA enters.)

BUD. I really like your dimple.
DEZA. See you in seven years.

(Lights fade on the couple as she exits and #4 enters yelling. BUD is startled out of his dream.)

#4. Get up! They're trying to sneak it out early! Get up! They're fixing to take off! *(He hurries off. People are running all over Hooverville.)*
BUGS. Come on, Bud, we got to get on that train!

(BUD tosses his blanket into his suitcase, ties it, and the boys quickly exit the shanty. #5 sticks his head out.)

#5. Hey, Slim, is this your paper?
BUD *(to BUGS)*. I'll catch you; go ahead. *(To #5.)* Thanks a lot! *(Clutches the flyer. The hissing of the train is heard. The crowd freezes.)*
ALL. The locomotive was hissing and spitting coal-black smoke into the sky.
#5. A big shower of sparks would glow up from inside the dark cloud.
#7. Making it look like a gigantic black genie was trying to raise up out of the smokestack.

(POLICE CAPTAIN [JAKE] and OFFICERS clad in police attire and bathed in blue and red move in to impede the crowd. JAKE speaks through a horn.)

JAKE. The police are on the way and they have orders to shoot anyone who tries to get on this train.
#4. I'd rather be shot than sit around and watch my kids go hungry.

(The crowd takes a step.)

JAKE. Hold steady, men.
POLICE OFFICER. Jake, there's four hundred men out there and more coming. Mr. Pinkerton ain't paying me enough to do this. *(OFFICER tosses his hat and club to the ground and exits. The train whistle blows. It starts to chug away.)*
ALL. The big steel wheels started moving. *(More hats hit the stage.)*
BUD. It was like someone said—
#4. On your mark, get set, go!

(BUD is dropped to the floor in the stampede. He is lifted to his feet.)

BUGS. Bud, throw your bag, throw me your bag! *(BUD tosses the bag. BUGS catches it but the blue flyer flies out.)*
BUD. It was like a miracle; it landed in my hand.
BUGS. Bud, don't stop! Run!
BUD. My legs were gone. *(BUGS throws the bag from the train as the train and all its passengers exits.)* Man, I'd

found some family and he was gone before we could really get to know each other. Man, this is one tough suitcase.

(Gunshots are heard off stage. JAKE enters with OFFICERS.)

BUD. A bunch of cops were standing around with pistols out. The fire was burning bigger than ever.

JAKE. The cops were tearing all the shacks down and were throwing the wood and cardboard and hunks of cloth into the middle of the fire.

DEZA'S MOM. You yellow-belly lowlifes. You waited till you knew the men was gone.

(JAKE takes the large pot and fires down into it.)

BUD. I tried to see if I could spot Deza Malone. *(BUD wanders away and plops himself on the ground.)* It seems like the only good thing that came out of going to Hooverville was that I finally kissed a girl. How could her father find them now? *(He looks down at the flyer in his hand, takes out his mother's photo and examines them.)* Maybe it came floating back to me because this Herman E. Calloway really was my father. Momma must've known she wasn't going to be around too long and was trying to leave me a message about who my daddy was. That idea dug its roots in deep and started spreading out.

Scene 9

(The scene shifts back to the library.)

BUD. I found Flint and Grand Rapids. 120. Wow! 120, divided by 5, that meant I'd have to walk for 24 hours to reach Grand Rapids; one whole day and one whole night. By this time tomorrow I'd be looking at the face of the man who had to be my father.

(BUD exits. #6 walks on stage and approaches the audience. As he finishes speaking he becomes a tree.)

#6. If you look at a great big maple tree it's hard to believe it started out as a little seed.

(A musical instrument softly starts to play. #7 enters speaking. Becomes a tree.)

#7. I mean there's no way your brain will buy that this little thing can grow up into something so big you have to bend your neck back just to see the top of it.

(A couple more instruments come in as #2 enters. Another tree.)

#2. Something so big that you can hang a swing on it.

(The tempo increases as more instruments come in with #1. Another tree.)

#1. Or build a tree house in it.

(The rest of the ENSEMBLE enters. We build to a crescendo with the end of #4's line. Another tree.)

#4. Or drive a car into it and kill yourself and any bad-lucked passengers that might be taking a ride with you.

BUD. Ideas are a lot like that. *(BUD pulls out the blue flyer and quickly replaces it.)* The idea of Herman E. Calloway being my father started as something so teeny that if I hadn't paid it no mind it would've blown away with the first good puff of wind. But it had gone and sneaked itself into being a mighty maple, big enough that I made up my mind to walk 120 miles clean across the state of Michigan.

Scene 10

(Light shift. ENSEMBLE become animals. We discover a sign saying YOU ARE NOW LEAVING FLINT. BUD watches a toad snatch insects out of the air, as a mouse plays a strange game with a rat. All are being eyed by an owl. Somewhere a snake lurks. BUD is caught in the middle of their games; he is both frightened and fascinated.)

#1 [BUG]. Bugzzz.

#2 [TOAD]. And toady-frogs.

#3 [MOUSE]. Mice and rats.

(The SNAKE inches toward the unsuspecting rodents.)

#1 [BUG]. Play a dangerous…

BUD. …scary…
#1 [BUG]. Kind of hide—
#2 [TOAD]. And-go-seek.
#3 [MOUSE]. Where they rustle around and try to keep away from each other.
#1 [BUG]. Or try to find each other.
BUD. Instead of being tagged and called "it" like the way human beans play the game.

(The SNAKE moves to within striking distance of the MOUSE.)

#4 [SNAKE]. Out here the ones that got got.
#7 [OWL]. Got ate up.

(OWL swoops down upon the SNAKE, hooting. All bolt for exits, leaving BUD. He watches the OWL eat. CAT yowls are heard off stage. A car goes by and BUD ducks in the bushes until it's gone.)

BUD. Flint ended all of a sudden. Here you have Flint and a sidewalk. *(BUD jumps in and out of Flint several times. Stops. Catches his breath. Looks around. A CAT yowl is heard. A car goes by and BUD ducks in the bushes until it's gone.)* I felt like I'd been walking all night.

(A car stops. BUD dives for cover. A man [LEFTY] gets out, scans the woods and whistles. He whistles again.)

LEFTY. Say hey… Say hey! I know my eyes aren't what they used to be, but I know they aren't so bad that they'd lie to me about seeing a young brown-skinned boy walking along the road just outside of Owasso, Michigan, at two-thirty in the morning.

BUD. I couldn't tell if he was talking to me or to hisself.

LEFTY. And I'ma tell you, I've seen some things out of place before and a young brown-skinned boy walking along a road just outside of Owasso, Michigan, at two-thirty in the morning is definitely not where he ought to be. In fact, neither one of us should be out here this time of night. Son, this is no time to play. Are you from Flint?

BUD. I wonder how grown folks know so doggone much.

LEFTY. You know what? Just so happens that I've got a spare baloney and mustard sandwich and an apple.

BUD. Shucks.

LEFTY. Might even have some extra red pop.

BUD. But I don't like mustard, sir. *(BUD slaps his hands over his mouth.)*

LEFTY. Well, I don't suppose the mustard's been glued on; I'll bet you we can scrape it off. What do you say?

BUD. Just leave them at the side of the road and I'll get them. And please open the bottle of pop, sir, I don't have a bottle key on me.

LEFTY. Oh, no, can't do that. The deal is I feed you, you show me your face. *(BUD steps out. They face each other.)* A deal's a deal. Here it is. *(LEFTY removes a brown paper bag and a glowing bottle of red soda from the car.)*

BUD. Could you put them down and I'll eat them and you can keep driving, sir?

LEFTY. I've got a little time to spare. *(Hypnotized, BUD reaches for the soda, and LEFTY raises it above his head.)* Hold on now. I've got a problem and I need you to help me figure it out.

BUD. Uh-oh. What he'd just said is—

(Music.)

ANNOUNCER. Bud Caldwell's Rules and Things for Making a Better Liar Out of Yourself Number 87.

(Fanfare.)

BUD. **When a adult tells you they need your help with a problem, get ready to be tricked. Most time this means they just want you to go fetch something for them.**

LEFTY. My problem is I'm not quite as brave as you are. And the sooner you can put my mind at ease about what you're doing out here the sooner we both can go about our business, OK… Well?

BUD. Nothing, sir.

LEFTY. What's your name son?

BUD. Bud, not Buddy, sir.

LEFTY. Did you run away from home, Bud-not-Buddy?

BUD. This guy was making fun of me. Yes, sir.

LEFTY. OK, that's a start. *(He hands BUD the soda. BUD starts slamming it down. After a moment LEFTY starts tugging on the bottle.)* Hold on, hold on, don't belt it all down on the first pull. Home, where is that?

BUD. No matter what I told him this man wasn't going to let me stay out here by myself, but he was making things seem so scary that not staying out here was OK.

LEFTY. Where's home, Bud?

BUD. I ran away from Grand Rapids, sir.

LEFTY. Grand Rapids!

BUD. Yes, sir. My brain came up with the perfect lie.

LEFTY. Well I'll be…that's where I'm from; I left there not an hour and a half ago. *(They retrieve BUD's bag, LEFTY holding on to BUD's arm the whole time.)* Bud-not-Buddy, you don't know how lucky you are I came through here. Some of these folks used to have a sign hanging along here that said, and I'm going to clean up the language for you, it said, "To Our Negro Friends Who Are Passing Through, Kindly Don't Let the Sun Set on Your Rear End in Owosso!"

(They move to the car. BUD looks in the window. There is a box in the car. BUD reads what it says.)

BUD. URGENT: CONTAINS HUMAN BLOOD!!! Oh man!

LEFTY. Get in. I'm going back to Grand Rapids tomorrow. *(He lets go of BUD's arm. BUD locks the car doors and pulls his knife free.)*

BUD. The only kind of people who would carry human blood around in a car were vampires! *(BUD shifts gears and takes off.)* Wow! If I kept things like this up I would knock Baby Face Nelson off the FBI's ten most wanted!

(The engine bucks and dies. LEFTY raps on the car.)

LEFTY. Roll the window down for a minute, Bud.

BUD. Sometimes it's terrible to have been brought up proper. *(BUD unrolls the window a crack.)*

LEFTY. OK, what's this?

BUD. How come you're carrying real human blood around in your car? I know how to kill vampires. This knife is genuine solid twenty-four-carat silver.

LEFTY. Sweet baby Jesus, why me? Bud, If I was a vampire why have I got that sandwich and bottle of red pop?

BUD. …Bait!

LEFTY. Bud, if I was a vampire I'd just stick my fangs into one of those bottles and have my supper. Besides, where've you ever heard of a vampire that knew how to drive a car?

BUD. That made sense. Could I please see your teeth, sir?

LEFTY. What?

BUD. Your teeth, sir. *(LEFTY mumbles to himself and opens his mouth.)* They look like they could bite a pretty good grapefruit-sized chunk out of you.

LEFTY. Bud, I've got to get this blood to Flint, they need it right away for someone's operation. I can tell you're far too smart to believe in any nonsense like vampires, son. Be a good boy and open the door. *(BUD unlocks the door. LEFTY gets in and drives off.)* Thank God you don't know how to drive.

BUD. If you'da showed me some fangs I'da learned real quick. I wasn't never going to get away from this doggone city.

Scene 11

(LEFTY drives.)

LEFTY. Son, there just aren't too many places a young Negro boy should be traveling by himself, especially not clear across Michigan. There're folks in this state that make your average Ku Kluxer look like John Brown. You know who John Brown is?

BUD. Uh-uh, no, sir.

LEFTY. That's all right, he's out there moldering somewhere. The point is you were very lucky this time. Don't you feel bad about worrying your mother like this, Bud-not-Buddy?

BUD. My mother is dead, sir. Most times if you tell a adult that they'll leave you alone.

LEFTY. I'm sorry to hear that, Bud. So you stay with your daddy?

BUD. Yes, sir.

LEFTY. What's his name?

BUD. His name is Herman E. Calloway, and he—

LEFTY. What??? I know your father; everybody in Grand Rapids does. At first glimpse I wouldn't say you look that much like Herman. *(He gives BUD the sandwich and pop.)* Bud, my name's Mr. Lewis. Now if you were twenty years older you could call me Lefty. But you're not, so you can't.

BUD. Yes, sir, Mr. Lewis, sir.

LEFTY. I just know I'll be having nightmares about meeting you for the rest of my life. I'll be deep in the middle of a Ruth Dandridge dream, when all of a sudden I'll be seeing my car and that blood pulling away with nothing of you showing but that little peanut-head of yours peeking up over the dash. Anyone ever tell you you've got a little peanut-head?

BUD. No, sir.

LEFTY. You look like one of George Washington Carver's experiments sprouted legs and run off. Bud, I am teasing. Uh-oh.

(A flashing red light appears accompanied by a siren.)

BUD. Uh-oh was right!

(BUD crouches down in his seat as the POLICE approach.)

COP. Pull the car over to the side of the road.

LEFTY. Bud, listen very carefully to what I'm going to tell you and do exactly as I say.

BUD. What he just said about listening carefully and doing exactly what he said was—

(Siren out.)

BUD. Rules and Things Number 8.

(We hear the sound of BUD's heartbeat.)

BUD. **Whenever a adult tells you to listen carefully and talks to you in a real calm voice, do not listen, run as fast as you can because something real terrible is just around the corner. Especially if the cops are chasing you.**

LEFTY. Bud, close your mouth. Now I want you to take the box and quickly put it all the way beneath your seat. Now stay put and don't say anything. Good boy. *(LEFTY exits the car and moves toward the COP.)*

BUD. OK, I'ma count to ten, then I'm going to snatch my suitcase and book out for those buildings. One—

COP. I want to look in the trunk.

BUD. 7, 8, 9, 10. OK, this time I'm really, *really* going to grab the doggone— *(There is a loud bang. BUD jerks around. LEFTY slowly and deliberately stretches his hands to the sky and backs away.)*

LEFTY. It was only Mr. Lewis closing the trunk. *(LEFTY and the COP return to the side of the car.)*

COP. What's in the suitcase?

LEFTY. Those are Bud's things. I'm taking him home to Grand Rapids.

COP. Oh, your grandson, huh? You two look just alike.

LEFTY. Why, thank you, Officer; I always thought the boy was unusually handsome.

COP. The cop didn't have a good sense of humor. There've been reports that some more of those stinking labor organizers might be sneaking up here from Detroit.

LEFTY. You don't say.

COP. Drive carefully.

(LEFTY returns to his seat. After a moment, he composes himself. The heartbeat stops.)

LEFTY. First I save you from being eaten by some vampires in Owosso, then that police officer saves you from the feared and loathsome labor organizers of Detroit! *(He produces a flyer for a labor meeting from the box*

BUD has hidden.) You are truly blessed. You sleepy? We can have our talk in the morning. Here. *(He pulls a jacket from the back seat and hands it to BUD.)*

BUD. The jacket smelled like spice and soap.

LEFTY. Oh, Bud-not-Buddy. Could you reach over into that box and hand me one of those bottles of blood? I haven't had a bite to eat all day.

(BUD reaches for the box and stops himself. He smiles.)

BUD. I'd never heard of a vampire that could drive a car and I'd never seen one that had such a good sense of humor. I knew I was safe.

(BUD pulls the jacket over his head. Lights shift. BUD wakes.)

LEFTY. Good morning, Walking Willie. I thought you'd left the earth for good. When we dropped that blood off at Hurley Hospital, I got in touch with your daddy and let him know you were all right.

BUD. Uh-oh. What did he say, sir?

LEFTY. I sent a telegram to the Log Cabin. He still owns that club, doesn't he?

BUD. Yes, sir.

LEFTY. Looking familiar?

BUD. Uh-oh. Yes, sir. I pointed at a gasoline filling station and said, "Yup, there's the gasoline filling station." My heart started jumping around in my stomach. Uh-oh. A sign said—

ANNOUNCER. APPEARING FRIDAY THROUGH SUNDAY IN JULY, HERMAN E. CALLOWAY AND THE NUBIAN KNIGHTS OF THE NEW DEAL.

LEFTY. He's here.

BUD. Mr. Lewis, can I go talk to my father by myself, sir?

LEFTY. Bud, you just ran away from that man all the way across the state; I think I'd better hand-deliver you.

BUD. I swear I'll turn myself in to him.

LEFTY *(grabs ahold of BUD's suitcase)*. Bud, you don't go anywhere without this, do you?

BUD. No, sir.

LEFTY. OK, I'll give you…five minutes to talk to your dad alone. If you're not back by then I'll bring your bag in for you.

BUD. The building looked like it was made out of giant chopped-down trees. I knew this was one of those doors that Momma had been talking about. *(He opens the door.)* Shucks, there was another set of regular doors inside. I waited. *(He goes back to the car.)* He's in there; he was so glad to see me that I'm not even in a whole lot of trouble. He's real busy and told me to tell you thank you.

LEFTY. Well, I expect you're gonna be having problems sitting down before the night's over. OK, tell your daddy I said hello.

BUD. Thank you, Mr. Lewis. *(He stands waving until LEFTY has pulled away.)* This time I pushed the second set of doors open and walked in.

(Lights out. END OF ACT ONE.)

ACT TWO

Scene 1

(Light shift. Five men are revealed on a small stage. They are watching a sixth who has his back to BUD. DOUG THE THUG is beating a tattoo on the stage with his sticks. JIMMY is cleaning his trumpet.)

DOO-DOO-BUG. There were six men sitting on a little stage.

BUD. One of them was white. The guy who had to be my father was sitting with his back to me.

HERMAN E. CALLOWAY. That's right, after I won the Golden Gloves…

BUD. He was talking just like me!

DOO-DOO-BUG. It didn't take much listening to tell he was lying.

DIRTY DEED. Or at least doing some real good exaggerating.

HERMAN E. CALLOWAY. No one couldn't tell me I wasn't going to be middleweight champ within two, three years tops.

DUG THE THUG. Middleweight? What, this was so long ago gravity wasn't as strong as it is now, or did a pound just weigh less back then? *(Laughter from the band.)*

HERMAN E. CALLOWAY. You got to keep in mind that I had more hair and fewer pounds back then. *(CALLOWAY removes his hat.)*

BUD. My dad shaves his hair!

HERMAN E. CALLOWAY. My manager lines up a bout against a fighter by the name of Jordan "Snaggletooth" MacNevin. I'm expecting some young Irish kid with bad teeth but this guy was one of us and so old that he could have been a waiter at the Last Supper. I wasn't about to show mercy; I go out and flick this halfway stiff right jab clean at Pops' head and—

JIMMY. Herman, to this day I can't believe you swung at that old man.

HERMAN E. CALLOWAY. I wasn't trying to kill him, Jimmy. I just wanted to put him down quick and quiet.

JIMMY. Uh, uh, uh…

HERMAN E. CALLOWAY. And the next thing I know I'm watching my mouthpiece and my chance to be champ flying out of the ring into the fourth row of seats. I ain't never been hit so hard in my life.

DUG THE THUG. What, you lost one fight and quit?

BUD. Then Herman E. Calloway said the words that let me know I was right:

HERMAN E. CALLOWAY. There comes a time when you're doing something and you realize it just doesn't make any sense to keep on doing it. You ain't being a quitter, it's just that the good Lord has seen fit to give you the sense to know; you understand, enough is enough.

BUD. The idea that had started as a teeny-weeny seed in a suitcase was now a mighty maple.

JIMMY. I thought I heard that door open. Did Miss Thomas send you, son?

(BUD makes a beeline for CALLOWAY.)

BUD. I had to see my father's face. My mighty maple started shaking in the wind. My dad's face was old, real old. But…there was just too much proof that this was my father! *(CALLOWAY smiles.)*

HERMAN E. CALLOWAY. Well, well, well, little man, what brings you here? *(CALLOWAY puts his hand over his eyes to shield them from the stage lights.)*

BUD. I'm here to meet my father.

JIMMY. Who's your daddy? Why'd he tell you to meet him here?

BUD. He didn't, sir. I come all the way from Flint to meet my daddy for the very first time. *(Everyone looks at the THUG, who stops drumming.)*

DUG THE THUG. Awww, man. Look, this child ain't no kin of mine.

BUD. You ain't my daddy. *(Points at CALLOWAY's mid-section.)* You know it's you. *(The circle of men get very quiet.)*

JIMMY. Hold on now, is your name Bud? Herman, don't you see? This has something to do with that crazy telegram you got this morning.

HERMAN E. CALLOWAY. First off, don't you be coming in here accusing folks of being your father, and second off, where is your mother?

BUD. Like he didn't already know. She's dead, sir.

HERMAN E. CALLOWAY. I am truly sorry to hear that, but it's obvious that you are a disturbed young man and you don't have a clue who your father is. You just tell us who's looking after you now, and we'll get you sent back to wherever it is you belong.

BUD. I belong with you now, sir.

HERMAN E. CALLOWAY. Now you look here…

JIMMY. Hold on, Herman. Bud, Mr. Calloway here can't be your daddy, no how, no way, nuh-uh. I don't know what gave you that idea, but whatever, we've got to get you back home. Someone in Flint's got to be worried sick about you.

BUD. No, sir, I don't have nobody left in Flint.

JIMMY. No one at all? No brothers, no sisters?

BUD. No, sir.

JIMMY. What about an auntie? No grandma?

BUD. Shucks, it looked like this guy was going to go over my whole family tree.

JIMMY. So were you living in an orphanage?

BUD. Uh-oh! Well, sir, I had some problems with some folks and after I hid their shotgun and poured water all over Todd Amos I busted out of the shed and had to go on the lam and then I thought it was about time I came and met my father because—

JIMMY. That's fine, son. What orphanage were you in?

BUD. Well, sir, I used to be in a Home and then I wasn't and then I was with some people that were kind of mean and then I tried to find Miss Hill but she moved all the way to Chicago and that was too far to wa—

JIMMY. Hold on, Bud. Do me a favor; go wait by that door for a minute. *(He points. BUD goes. JIMMY and CALLOWAY begin to whisper.)*

HERMAN E. CALLOWAY. Hey. But don't forget, this is your little red wagon; you pull it if you want.

JIMMY. Fair enough. *(He waves BUD over.)* Bud, we're all done rehearsing and were about to head over to the Sweet Pea. We'll feed you but you've got to tell us the truth.

BUD. What's the Sweet Pea, sir?

JIMMY. Best restaurant in Grand Rapids. Is it a deal?

BUD. I sure wasn't going to turn down my very first real restaurant food.

HERMAN E. CALLOWAY. Well, James, if he's gonna be doing some explaining it's got to be to you; I don't need to listen to this scamp's nonsense whilst I'm trying to digest my supper. *(CALLOWAY shoves an unlit pipe into his mouth and walks off the stage.)*

BUD. Shucks, I was starting to wish that Lefty Lewis or this James guy were my father.

JIMMY. Little man, my name is Jimmy Wesley, you can call me Mr. Jimmy. The drummer there is Doug "the Thug" Tennant the sax man is Harrison Eddie "Steady" Patrick.

STEADY EDDIE. Awww, man, it's not Eddie Steady, it's Steady Eddie, Steady Eddie Patrick.

JIMMY. Uh-huh. And on trombone we have Chug "Doo-Doo-Bug" Cross, and the palest member of the band, on piano, is Roy "Dirty Deed" Breed.

DUG THE THUG. I ain't trying to say that "Deed" ain't good on the eighty-eight keys, but you know the only reason he got this gig is 'cause he's Dutch, he's white.

STEADY EDDIE. Mr. C's always got a white fellow in the band, but he can't help that he was born that way.

DIRTY DEED. You're just too kind, Edward. How many folks you see living like us, Negro or white? Not many. That man may have his faults but I'm putting my hat in with him. It's against the law for a Negro to own property out here, Bud, so Mr. C put the Log Cabin in my name.

STEADY EDDIE. We get gigs playing polkas and waltzes and a lot of these white folks wouldn't hire us if they knew we were a Negro band, so Deed goes out and sets up everything.

JIMMY. Fellas, this here is Bud…what was your last name, Bud?

BUD. Caldwell, sir.

JIMMY. This here's Bud Caldwell. Y'all make the little man feel comfortable. *(The band overlaps their greetings to BUD.)*

DUG THE THUG. What's the word, Bud?

DIRTY DEED. How you doing?

DOO-DOO-BUG. Welcome, little stuff.

STEADY EDDIE. Good to meet you, my man.

BUD. Pleased to meet you.

JIMMY. All right, he'll ride over with you four; me and Herm will meet you there.

STEADY EDDIE. Come on, little man, grab that case over there. And be careful, that's my bread and butter in there. *(Beat.)* That's my horn, my ax, my saxophone—the thing I make all my money with, so don't get butterfingers and drop it.

BUD. Oh, yes, sir.

DUG THE THUG. Little secret, my man. I think the only reason Mr. C is denying he's your daddy is 'cause you went and hurt his feelings.

BUD. How? I didn't do nothing to him.

DUG THE THUG. There it is. Here you two are getting together for the first time and you didn't show the man no love. Doo-Doo-Bug. Bug, did you see any love being passed from this boy to his daddy?

DOO-DOO-BUG. You leave me out of your nonsense.

DUG THE THUG. You see, I know Mr. C better than most folks do. I know that beneath that coldhearted, evil, wicked, nasty, mean—

DOO-DOO-BUG. Don't forget cheap.

DUG THE THUG. You know cheap's right up high on the list. But beneath all that festering nastiness is a tender, kind, loving human being. When you get to the Sweet Pea, rush right up on him, yell out "Daddy," then plant a big juicy kiss right on the top of his shiny bald head.

STEADY EDDIE. Let's not get the little man killed before he's had a chance to eat, Thug. Son, you just steer clear of Mr. C for a while, and for God's sake, whatever you do don't call him Daddy or Poppa or give anyone the idea you two are kin, you hear?

BUD. Yes, sir. But isn't it just like my luck to come clean across the state to find my daddy and he turns out to be a mean old coot? *(BUD flinches realizing what he's said. The band is stunned.)* This was—

(Fanfare.)

ANNOUNCER. Bud Caldwell's Rules and Things Number 63.

BUD. **Never, ever say something bad about someone you don't know—especially when you're around a bunch of strangers. You never can tell who might be kin to that person or who might be a lip-flapping, big-mouth spy.**

(The THUG acts like he's writing down what BUD said.)

DUG THE THUG. Let's see, was that "mean old coot" or "old mean coot"? Shoot, baby—

STEADY EDDIE. Thug, you're gonna have to lay off the kid's chops; the little man's got problems enough.

BUD. Of all the Dusky Devestators of the Depression or the Nubian Knights, Steady Eddie is my favorite. *(BUD climbs into a car with the Nubian Knights.)*

DUG THE THUG. So, I'ma come right out and ask what's on everyone else's mind. How'd you find out Mr. C was your daddy?

BUD. My mother let me know.

DUG THE THUG. Uh, I'd never play the dozens on no one, but was your momma as old as sand when she had you. And was she blind?

BUD. No, sir, she was old, but her eyes didn't go bad yet. She was twenty when I was born, and she was twenty-six when she died. *(This silences the band.)*

DOO-DOO-BUG. THE SWEET PEA. *(The band echoes "The Sweet Pea," "Yeah the Pea," and the like. They climb out of the car.)*

DUG THE THUG. Things is hard all over, ain't they?

STEADY EDDIE. You're a tough little nut, I like that. Most folks your age would be bawling their eyes out if they got teased as hard as that fool drummer was teasing you, but you ain't even close to crying?

BUD. No, sir, my eyes don't cry no more.

STEADY EDDIE. "My eyes don't cry no more." You mind if I borrow that? Great name for a song.

BUD. No, sir, I don't mind at all.

STEADY EDDIE. Don't worry about the Thug, Mr. C changes drummers the way most folks change their drawers.

Scene 2

(Shift to the inside of the Sweet Pea. All tables are full but one. The rest of the band is seated.)

BUD. It was like someone took a old pot and poured about a hundred gallons of hot apple cider and a hundred gallons of hot coffee into it.
STEADY EDDIE. Then stirred eight or nine sweet potato pies, crusts and all, into that.
DIRTY DEED. Then let six big steamy meat loafs float on top of all that.
DOO-DOO-BUG. Then threw in a couple handfuls of smashed potatoes.
DUG THE THUG. Then boiled the whole thing on high.
BUD. This must be exactly how heaven smells!
STEADY EDDIE. Over there, Bud.

(JIMMY points at BUD and waves him over.)

BUD. Shucks, I'd rather sit with the band than with Herman E. Calloway.
DUG THE THUG. Remember what I said. *(He points to the top of his head and mimes a bunch of kisses. BUD walks to MR. CALLOWAY's table.)*
JIMMY. Bud, this here's Miss Thomas, she's our vocal stylist. *(BUD is perplexed.)*

MISS THOMAS. I'm the singer, honey.

BUD. Pleased to meet you, ma'am. *(MISS THOMAS laughs and offers BUD her hand to shake.)* There were about nine diamond rings on just her right hand!

MISS THOMAS. Oh, my, a gentleman; I'm pleased to make your acquaintance as well. Come here, child.

BUD. Uh-oh. *(BUD puckers his lips and twists his face. MISS THOMAS pulls BUD's face up close.)*

MISS THOMAS. What's this, baby? *(She rubs a finger over the knots on his face.)*

BUD. They're vamp— That's just some hornet stings, ma'am; I got bit up when the Amoses locked me in their shed.

MISS THOMAS. When *who* locked you in *what* shed?

BUD. They were the people the home was paying to look after me. I got bit by their fish-head guards. *(He lifts his hand to her.)*

MISS THOMAS. My lord! Herman, this child's hand is infected. None of you men noticed how he looks?

HERMAN E. CALLOWAY. Talk to James.

JIMMY. Well, Grace, You know how dark it is in the Cabin, and, by God, there are some folks who just naturally have lopsided heads.

MISS THOMAS. Dark or not, even Blind Lemon Jefferson could see something's wrong with this baby's eye. What happened here, Bud? *(She taps BUD under the eye.)*

BUD. Well, ma'am, Todd Amos woke me up by shoving a pencil up my nose all the way to the R and I slapped him so we put up our dukes and it didn't take long before I knew I couldn't whip him so I just curled up and fell down. *(BUD looks CALLOWAY square in the face.)*

I fell down, ma'am, 'cause the Lord give me the good sense to know when enough is enough.

HERMAN E. CALLOWAY. Sounds like a case of diarrhea of the mouth and constipation of the brain.

MISS THOMAS. Where's your momma?

BUD. She died four years ago, ma'am.

MISS THOMAS. I'm sorry, sweetheart. How 'bout your daddy? Do you know where he's at? *(BUD points at CALLOWAY's stomach.)* Now, Bud, I can tell your momma did a fine job of raising you, so I'm kind of surprised that you're pointing like that. *(BUD lowers his hand.)*

HERMAN E. CALLOWAY. If you'll excuse me, this is about where I came in. *(He crosses to the rest of the band.)* All right. Someone's got to give me their seat and go sit with James and Miss Grace—oh, and my son. *(The entire band stands and starts to go.)*

STEADY EDDIE. Take my seat, Mr. C, I want to talk to that kid; he's got the look of a future sax man about him. *(STEADY EDDIE crosses to BUD's table.)*

MISS THOMAS. Do you mind if I order your supper, Bud?

BUD. No, ma'am. I thought they'd bring you whatever was on the stove.

TYLA. Y'all ready, Miss Thomas?

MISS THOMAS. We sure are, Tyla. Any more of that meat loaf left? *(TYLA indicates that there is.)* How about some okra and mashed potatoes too; does a glass of apple cider sound good?

BUD. Yes, ma'am, thank you, ma'am.

MISS THOMAS. OK. I'll have the same. *(TYLA silently takes orders from the rest of the table while BUD and*

MISS THOMAS talk. She exits to place them.) Bud, I'm pretty sure that there's just no way that Mr. C is your father. Tell me what gave you the idea he was.

BUD. My mother did, ma'am.

MISS THOMAS. Sweetheart, did you know Mr. C's pretty famous?

BUD. No, ma'am.

MISS THOMAS. Did she come right out and say, "Your daddy is Herman E. Calloway," Bud?

BUD. Uh-oh. As long as I kept Herman E. Calloway being my father to myself the whole thing made real good sense, but as soon as I tried to tell other folks about it, it seemed like something some stupid kid had dreamed up. Well…

(TYLA re-enters with a tray.)

MISS THOMAS. We'll talk tomorrow, Bud. *(Maybe this means BUD won't be sent back. TYLA delivers BUD a plate.)* No wonder you heard about rich folks going to restaurants once a week. It was the best meal I'd ever had. When it was done Miss Tyla brought me a dessert she called—

TYLA. On the house.

MISS THOMAS. It was a piece of warm sweet potato pie. *(MISS THOMAS begins to hum.)*

BUD. Miss Thomas must be the most beautiful woman in the world.

JIMMY. Her humming reminded me of the feeling you get when you walk barefoot on a railroad track.

STEADY EDDIE. Miss Thomas's humming made you feel like something big and strong was passing right by you.

JIMMY. It made you want to drop your fork and grab holt of something solid.

BUD. I could understand why Mr. Jimmy didn't call her a singer.

JIMMY. *Singer* wasn't a big enough word to take in the kind of music that was jumping out of Miss Thomas' chest.

BUD. And I didn't notice before how funny Mr. Jimmy was. And how nice Steady Eddie was either. *(A single instrument comes in soft and low.)* I'm not sure exactly when it happened, but another seed got to sprouting. *(Another instrument joins the first.)* All of a sudden I knew that of all the places in the world—

TYLA. This was the one. *(Yet another musical instrument rushes in.)*

BUD. That of all the people I'd ever met—

ALL BUT BUD & HERMAN E. CALLOWAY. These were the ones. *(All the instruments come crashing in. CALLOWAY slams his hands on the table and rises.)*

BUD. And Herman E. Calloway could kiss my wrist if he thought he was gonna scare me out of this. I was smiling and laughing and busting a gut so much that— *(BUD's laughter erupts into tears. The band cries out—)*

THE NUBIAN KNIGHTS. Woop, zoop, sloop. *(BUD covers his head, grabs his suitcase and runs outside.)*

BUD. Dangee, I'd never have any kind of reputation with the band now. *(MISS THOMAS follows. She hugs his head to her chest and rocks him back and forth.)*

MISS THOMAS. OK, baby, OK. I know, sweetheart, I know. *(She begins to hum. She speaks.)* Go ahead and cry, Bud, you're home.

Scene 3

(Lights shift to Grand Calloway Station. BUD is carrying his suitcase and MISS THOMAS is showing him into the house.)

MISS THOMAS. Now, Bud, this is what we call Grand Calloway Station. Mr. Calloway said that there were so many different people in and out of here that it reminded him of that train station in New York City. It's late, so I'll take you right up to where you're going to be sleeping. Miss Thomas opened a door. *(They enter a room. There is a bed and a dressing table between two small doors.)* On one side there was a bed and a window.

BUD. And on the other side were two little doors.

MISS THOMAS. OK. Do you think you'll be all right?

BUD. I would, except that those two little doors were just the right size for a young Frankenstein or Wolfman to come busting out.

MISS THOMAS. There's nothing in there but girls' clothes and toys.

BUD. Won't the girl get mad if she comes back in here and I'm sleeping in her bed?

MISS THOMAS *(beat)*. No, Bud, I don't think you have to worry about that, she's gone. *(She exits.)*

BUD. Uh-oh! That was two things to get nervous about in one sentence! The first thing was— *(Fanfare. BUD holds up his hand stopping the ANNOUNCER.)* Rules and Things Number 547, or something, about when a adult tells you, "Don't worry." The second bad thing was— *(BUD gestures for the ANNOUNCER to continue.)*

ANNOUNCER. Bud Caldwell's Rules and Things to Have a Funner Life and Make a Better Liar Out of Yourself Number 28.

(Fanfare.)

BUD. **Gone equals Dead!** I don't know why grown folks can't say someone is dead. That meant I was going to have to spend the night in the room of a little dead girl. I can never get why grown folks will put a kid all alone in a bedroom at night. It's just like they give the ghosts a treasure map and instead of there being a big pot of gold where X marks the spot, there's some poor kid that's sound asleep.

(CALLOWAY and MISS THOMAS enter arguing.)

MISS THOMAS. Herman E. Calloway!
HERMAN E. CALLOWAY. And Miss Thomas!
MISS THOMAS. Went at each other!
HERMAN E. CALLOWAY. They argued back!
MISS THOMAS. And forth! *(She points to BUD's room and exits.)*

(CALLOWAY crashes through the bedroom door.)

HERMAN E. CALLOWAY. The door banged open and Herman E. Calloway stood there huffing and puffing like the big bad wolf.
BUD. Only it looked like he'd already eaten the three little pigs.

(CALLOWAY glances at BUD then rushes to the set of doors and locks them. He crosses to BUD and speaks.)

HERMAN E. CALLOWAY. You've got the rest of them fooled but not me. I'm going to find out what your game is and believe you me, scamp, you're going back where you belong. *(CALLOWAY exits slamming the door and then re-enters.)* And you better not do any snooping around this room. I've got little secret bells all over everything and when something's stolen the bell goes off and only I can hear it, so watch your step. *(He exits.)*

MISS THOMAS *(off stage)*. You know, Herman, half the time I don't know if I should laugh at you or feel sorry for you.

BUD. What he said reminded me of what they used to tell us when they'd take us kids from the home to the YMCA to go swimming.

(We hear the shrill sound of a whistle and the LIFE-GUARD enters. BUD flops down on the bed.)

LIFEGUARD. We've had problems with you children urinating in the pool. This has forced the Y to put a special new kind of magic chemical in the water to turn water contaminated with urine a bright red. The chemical also causes severe burns to the skin of the urinater. So if a red cloud appears you will be arrested by the police, you will go to the hospital to fix your burns, you will go to jail and then your name will go on the list that says you can't swim in any building anywhere in the world. *(LIFEGUARD exits.)*

BUD. Shucks, nothing makes you want to pee in a pool more than someone who thinks you're stupid telling you not to do it; and nothing makes you want to steal something. It just didn't seem like it was true that he could be anyone's daddy. Man! Even though this was the bedroom of some little girl who kicked the bucket it felt like I was sleeping with my own blanket wrapped around my head. The best thing in the whole room was one wall that was covered with pictures of some horses cut out of a bunch of magazines.
MOMMA *(off stage)*. "Not me," said the horse.
BUD. The last thing I remember was—

(CALLOWAY has seeped into BUD's subconscious; he enters, his presence takes the form of a werewolf. It pounces on BUD's bed.)

HERMAN E. CALLOWAY. "Not me," said the Big Bad Wolf.
BUD. Even though a monster had gone and snucked hisself into the story, I didn't care— *(The CALLOWAY wolf exits.)* nothing could hurt me now. *(Lights out on BUD.)*

Scene 4

(Shift. Morning dances in on HERMAN E. CALLOWAY, MISS THOMAS, JIMMY and STEADY EDDIE who are revealed mid conversation drinking coffee.)

HERMAN E. CALLOWAY. So that's how the cookie's going to crumble.

MISS THOMAS. You have no idea how bad those orphanages can be. I can't believe you. You'll take care of any stray dog wandering through this neighborhood, but when it comes to a child all of a sudden you have no sympathy.

(Lights up on BUD in bed.)

BUD. I was dreaming. There was a neat pile of clothes folded the same way Momma used to fold them. She would always leave a note.
MOMMA *(off stage)*. Dear Bud, please be neater, see you tonight, I love you.

(BUD looks under the covers. He dresses in bed.)

BUD. Aw, shucks, Miss Thomas must've undressed me.
MISS THOMAS. We agreed last night what we were going to do about that boy. I already got him some clothes.
HERMAN E. CALLOWAY. I'ma find out what the real story is, and then we'll see.

(BUD crawls out of bed.)

BUD. Man, my first new pair of trousers. *(He stuffs his underwear in his pants and creeps downstairs.)* It's too embarrassing to have strangers look at your dirty drawers.
MISS THOMAS. I believe the child. You, above all people should know that I've got a sense about when someone's lying.
BUD. Uh-oh. I'd have to remember that.

MISS THOMAS. Until we've heard otherwise, he's staying right here.

STEADY EDDIE. Well, I'm glad to hear it. I think he's going to like this.

BUD. A present. *(BUD quickly tiptoes back to his room so he can make noise coming back down.)* Good morning, Mr. Calloway. I didn't mean it. Good morning, Miss Thomas, Mr. Jimmy, Steady Eddie.

ALL BUT HERMAN E. CALLOWAY. Good morning, Bud.

(CALLOWAY heads for the door. He speaks as he exits.)

HERMAN E. CALLOWAY. I don't like the way Loudean is sounding; I'ma have a look at her plugs.

JIMMY. So what's the scoop, little man? Cop a squat.

(BUD is unsure what this means. Finally, he sits.)

MISS THOMAS. Were your ears burning last night, Bud?

BUD *(grabs his ears)*. No, ma'am.

MISS THOMAS. We've got to talk to some people in Flint first, but we were hoping that you'd stay here for a while. I'm going to assume that that smile means yes.

BUD. Yes, ma'am! Thank you, ma'am!

MISS THOMAS. Before that grin gets stuck on your face, Bud, there's one person in particular that you're going to have to be very patient with. Do you know who I mean?

BUD. It's Mr. Calloway.

MISS THOMAS. Good boy. Bud, I'm concerned about your spirit. Lord knows Mr. Calloway is going to give it a test.

BUD. My spirit's a lot stronger than it looks; most folks are surprised by that. Then she did something that made me feel strange.

(MISS THOMAS grabs BUD the same way as his mom, repeats the same gesture and looks him real hard in the face.)

MISS THOMAS. Really, Bud, this might get hard for you. I don't always travel with the band, so I don't want you to forget what I'm telling you.

BUD. No, ma'am, I won't.

MISS THOMAS. Bud, something tells me you are a godsend to us.

STEADY EDDIE. Since you're going to be part of the family there're some things we've got to talk about. Now I've noticed the tight grip you keep on that old suitcase of your'n. I need to know how attached to it you are.

BUD. I carry it with me everywhere I go.

STEADY EDDIE. Are you attached to the suitcase, or is it the things inside that are important?

BUD. The things I got from my mother are the most important.

STEADY EDDIE. Good, 'cause it just wouldn't look too copacetic for you to be carrying that ratty old bag. This is my old alto saxophone case; I figured you might as well keep your momma's things in it.

BUD. Wow! Thank you, Steady Eddie! There was a real old smell that came out of it, like dried-up slobber and something dead. It smelled great!

Scene 5

(The rest of the band enters.)

BUD. I'm going to be going around with you.
DIRTY DEED. Glad to have you on board, partner.
STEADY EDDIE. I was just about to tell him some of the things Herman E. Calloway requires of anybody in his band.
DUG THE THUG. Otherwise known as Herman E. Calloway's Rules to Guarantee You Have No Female Companionship, No Alcohol and No Fun at All.
STEADY EDDIE. Rule number one, practice two hours a day.
JIMMY. That's a good one.
STEADY EDDIE. So I got you this, Bud. It's called a recorder. Once you've developed a little wind, and some tone and a embouchure we'll move on to something a little more complicated.
BUD. Man, all these Grand Rapids people really do talk funny. Thank you!
DUG THE THUG. Now all that's left is to give little stuff here a name.
MISS THOMAS. You know, I don't like the way Loudean's been sounding; I think I'm gonna go check the air in the trunk.
DOO-DOO-BUG. You don't have to leave.
MISS THOMAS. Darling, I know that, it's just that this is one of those man things that you all think is so mysterious and special that I have absolutely no interest in. *(She exits.)*

STEADY EDDIE. Hand me your ax and stand up, Bud. Uh-uh, she was right, this is mysterious and special, so that grin's got to go, brother. Mr. Jimmy.

JIMMY. Gentlemen, the floor's open for names for our newest member of the band, Bud-not-Buddy.

(Hands go up and the THUG is called on.)

DUG THE THUG. Mr. Chairman, in light of the boy's performance last night at the Sweet Pea, I nominate the name Waterworks Willie.

BUD. Shucks.

JIMMY. You're out of order, Douglas.

(STEADY EDDIE is called on.)

STEADY EDDIE. Mr. Chairman, this boy's obviously going to be a musician; he slept until twelve-thirty today, so I propose that we call him Sleepy.

JIMMY. The name Sleepy is before the board.

DIRTY DEED. We need something that lets folks know how slim the boy is.

DOO-DOO-BUG. How about the Bone?

STEADY EDDIE. Not enough class.

JIMMY. How do you say *bone* in French?

DUG THE THUG. *Bone* in French is *la bone.*

DOO-DOO-BUG. *La bone*, nah, it don't have a ring to it.

STEADY EDDIE. How about Sleepy LaBone?

(BUD's face cracks into a smile the size of Texas.)

BUD. That was about the best name I'd ever heard in my life!

(Music.)

JIMMY. Let's try it out.

ANNOUNCER. Ladies and gentlemen, thank you very much for coming out on this cold November night, this night that will live in history, this night that for the first time on any stage anywhere, you have listened to the smooth saxophonical musings of that prodigy of the reed, Mr. *(fanfare)* Sleepy Labone!

(The band explodes into applause. They overlap their appreciation.)

DUG THE THUG. What can I say but *bang*.

DIRTY DEED. You nailed him!

DOO-DOO-BUG. My man!

JIMMY. Kneel down, young man. *(JIMMY knights BUD with the recorder.)* Arise and welcome to the band, Mr. Sleepy LaBone.

(BUD rises, all celebrate as CALLOWAY enters and drops a mop bucket at BUD's feet.)

Scene 6

(We shift back to the Log Cabin. The band is setting up their instruments while BUD mops the floor.)

DOO-DOO-BUG. Herman E. Calloway was trying to work Bud like a dog.

BUD. Herman E. Calloway didn't even know how much fun I was having. *(BUD glances at the band, looks at the hand-operated wringer on the mop bucket, looks at the mop and speaks to it.)* Somebody was at a washing machine not paying attention— *(BUD shoves the mop head into the wringer and pushes down the handle.)* to what he was doing and getting his whole body pulled through and wrungeded out. I let the handle up to see what was left of this poor soul.

DIRTY DEED. One, two, one two three!

DUG THE THUG. The Thug was brushing his sticks across the round gold metal thing next to his drums and making it sound like a soft rain was commencing to fall on someone's tin roof.

DIRTY DEED. Then Dirty Deed started making the piano fall right in with the rain pats the Thug was making.

BUD. It made you think of what Niagara Falls must sound like.

STEADY EDDIE. Steady Eddie made his ax talk.

(STEADY starts to blow. MISS THOMAS enters with JIMMY and CALLOWAY. MISS THOMAS rubs BUD's head, startling him slightly.)

MISS THOMAS. Bud, the place is sparkling.

(CALLOWAY grunts and heads onto the stage and lifts the neck of his bass.)

JIMMY. Mr. Jimmy joined in the storm.

HERMAN E. CALLOWAY. Herman E. Calloway patted the strings.

BUD. It seemed like he was the thunder.

HERMAN E. CALLOWAY. Soft and far away but getting closer all the time.

JIMMY. All the instruments blended up together!

BUD. And just like that smell in the library, you'd have a real hard time trying to figure out which instrument was your favorite. Until Miss Thomas opened her mouth. While the rest of the band was being a storm—

MISS THOMAS. She was the sun busting through thick, gray clouds.

BUD. It should be called Miss Thomas and the Dusky Devastators of the Depression and a Mean Old Guy on the Giant Fiddle.

MISS THOMAS. La da de da de da da, ha whee a ho, ha whee a ho, ha whee a day.

BUD. She was so good she didn't even have to sing real words. In the end—

STEADY EDDIE. It was Miss Thomas' voice—

BUD. And Steady's saxophone doing all that talking that you really wanted to listen to.

MISS THOMAS. Doe de doe de doe de bahs.

BUD. Just when you thought you could understand this language, Miss Thomas broke out in American.

MISS THOMAS. What's new? We haven't met since then, gee, but it's nice to see you again, nice to see you again, nice to see you again.

JIMMY. And the storm was over.

(Shift. The band finishing its set. ANNOUNCER blows through cities introducing the band.)

ANNOUNCER. Thank you, Sturgis, we are Herman E. Calloway and the Gifted Gents of Gospel—featuring Miss Grace "Blessed" Thomas' vocals!!!

(Applause. Light shift. MISS THOMAS exits.)

ANNOUNCER. Good evening, Preston! We are Herman E. Calloway and the Terminally Unhappy Blues Band. Masters of the Delta blues!!!

(Applause. Light shift.)

ANNOUNCER. Good night, Kentland, and thank you. We are H.E. Callowski and the Wonderful Warblers of Warsaw. Masters of the polka!!!

(Applause. Light shift.)

BUD. I'd heard the band play and practice a thousand times and still had to just about sit on my hands when they were finished so I wouldn't bust out clapping.

Scene 7

(BUD is helping the band pack up and leave Kentland.)

JIMMY. Bud, you can ride back with Herman.
BUD. Uh-oh.
HERMAN E. CALLOWAY. Whatever.

(JIMMY and the band climb into the other car and take off for Grand Calloway Station. BUD practices the recorder.)

BUD. Shucks, a whole hour and a half trapped in a car with him.
HERMAN E. CALLOWAY. Herman E. Calloway started nudging things around with the toe of his shoe.
BUD. I could see that it was just rocks.

(CALLOWAY grunts and stretches his arm toward the ground.)

HERMAN E. CALLOWAY. He started to bend over, but… *(Grunts.)* Make yourself useful, boy, and hand me this one.
BUD *(picking up the stone)*. It was the exact same kind of rock I'd use if I was about to chunk someone in the head. *(BUD hands the stone to CALLOWAY; he half expects to get pelted with it. CALLOWAY places it in his pocket.)* Mr. C, wasn't that just a rock?
HERMAN E. CALLOWAY. Sure was. He climbed in the Packard. And opened the glove box. *(He opens the glove box as BUD climbs in the passenger side.)* Bad habit.

BUD. There weren't any gloves or maps, just a bunch of perfect throwing rocks. *(Grabbing a couple he reads.)* idlewild m. 5 dot 2 dot 36. chicago il. 3 dot 19 dot 32. I've got some of these, sir.

HERMAN E. CALLOWAY. Bud, I know you're not the sharpest knife in the drawer, and I hate to be the bearer of bad tidings, but those are found all over the world. In fact, they're about as common as rocks.

BUD. Yes, sir, but mine have writing on them too.

HERMAN E. CALLOWAY. Hmmm.

BUD. You don't believe me. I'll show you. *(He places the rocks back in the glove box, retrieves two rocks from his sax case.)*

HERMAN E. CALLOWAY. We got back to Grand Calloway station.

BUD. See, the only difference is mine say flint m. dot 8 dot 11 dot 11 and gary in. dot 6 dot 13 dot 12.

HERMAN E. CALLOWAY. Where did you find these? Didn't I tell you not to do any rummaging around in that room?

(CALLOWAY snatches the rocks from BUD's hand. JIMMY walks out of Grand Calloway Station to remove one last box from the other car. He gives an unnoticed wave.)

HERMAN E. CALLOWAY. Well, where'd you get these?

BUD. If I could get my hands back on my rocks I knew I could outrun Mr. C.

HERMAN E. CALLOWAY. Answer me, where'd you take these from!!!

(JIMMY runs over to break them up, just as CALLOWAY balls up his fists and raises them.)

JIMMY. Herman? What's this? What's wrong?

HERMAN E. CALLOWAY. I told you about this boy from the word go. He's been snooping through things in the house that he's got no business in; he stole these.

BUD. No, sir, I did not.

HERMAN E. CALLOWAY. Then where'd you get them? I'm not going to ask you again.

BUD. I was surprised they hadn't turned into diamonds or dust.

(JIMMY takes the rocks from CALLOWAY and reads.)

JIMMY. Flint, Michigan, August eleven, 1911, and Gary, Indiana, June thirteenth, 1912? That's more than twenty-five years ago. Son, where'd you find these? Just tell the truth.

BUD. I got them from my momma and that's the swear-'fore-God truth. Now could I please have my rocks back, sir.

HERMAN E. CALLOWAY/JIMMY. Your momma?

BUD *(sticks out his hand)*. Yes, sir.

JIMMY. Bud, what did you say your momma's name was?

BUD. No one ever asked me, sir.

HERMAN E. CALLOWAY. You throw a lot of "sirs" around but you've still got a real strong, real smart-mouthed, disrespectful streak in you, boy. Now you answer the question or I'll—

BUD. Angela, sir. Angela Janet Caldwell. I didn't mean to say sir.

JIMMY. Lord have mercy…

HERMAN E. CALLOWAY. Herman E. Calloway stumbled and fumbled into Grand Calloway Station.

JIMMY. Like he'd been struck blind. *(He exits.)*

BUD. Herman E. Calloway was the best liar in the world. I knew it! I knew he was my father!

JIMMY. Bud, he's not your father.

BUD. Yes, sir, he is. That's why he run off like that; he got caught lying after all these years!

JIMMY. Bud, that's enough. Herman is not your father. But Angela Janet is his daughter's name. If what you're saying is true, Lord help us all, it looks like Herman might be your grandfather.

BUD. I was glad that Herman E. Calloway wasn't my dad. Shucks, who'd want a daddy that on top of being so old and so doggone mean had such a big belly? Not me.

Scene 8

(We move into Grand Calloway Station where MISS THOMAS, BUD and JIMMY stand outside CALLOWAY's door.)

JIMMY. Herman. Herman?

MISS THOMAS. Herman. *(JIMMY pulls BUD aside and sets him at the kitchen table. MISS THOMAS follows.)* My, my, my.

JIMMY. Now look here, Bud. You're sure your momma's name was Angela Janet?

BUD. Yes, sir.

JIMMY. And her last name was Caldwell too; she never said nothing about being no Calloway?

BUD. No, sir, her name was Caldwell.

JIMMY. OK, OK, Bud, how'd your momma pass?

BUD. *Pass* was just like *gone*. She was too sick to go to work for six days in a row. Then one morning I went into her room and she was dead.

JIMMY. Bud, what'd your momma look like?

MISS THOMAS. James, what are you insinuating? Look at Bud's eyes; you have to ask if this is Herman's grandchild?

JIMMY. Now hold on, Grace, I'm just trying to ask the questions I know Herman'd ask if he could. Bud, was she short or tall; was she slim or big-boned?

MISS THOMAS. James—

BUD. Pardon me, ma'am, I know how I can show you what she looks like. *(He goes to his sax case and pulls out his mother's photo. He hands it to MISS THOMAS.)*

MISS THOMAS. Any more questions for this young man? *(She slides the picture over to JIMMY. He picks it up.)*

JIMMY. Well, I'll be. Uh, uh, uh, that definitely is Angela Janet Calloway! You sure this is your mother?

BUD. Yes, sir.

JIMMY. Well, I'll just be—

MISS THOMAS. There's little doubt about that, James, but what we've got to do…

BUD. That means that's not some little dead girl's room I'm sleeping in; that's my momma's room!

MISS THOMAS *(beat)*. That's right, Bud, you're back in your momma's room.

BUD. All he'd've had to do was call on us one time and I know she wouldn't have been so sad.

MISS THOMAS. Bud, give me your hand.

BUD. Uh-oh, pretty soon I'd have to come up with a Rules and Things about when Miss Thomas holds your hand.

MISS THOMAS. Bud, Mr. C—excuse me, your granddad didn't know anything about you. No one knew where your mother had gone.

JIMMY. She just up and run off one day. We all knew Herman was hard on her— "This is a hard world, especially for a Negro woman. She's got to be ready." Shoot, I could see that the girl wasn't the type to—

MISS THOMAS. James, why don't you check on Herman.

JIMMY. Oh. Oh, maybe I should. *(He exits.)*

MISS THOMAS. Bud, I know you can see your granddad has troubles getting along with most folks, right?

BUD. Yes, ma'am.

MISS THOMAS. He used to crow about how his mother and father had been born slaves and how now it was only two generations later and one of them was actually going to be a teacher. It was his dream, not hers. The more he pushed her, the more she fought him. Finally she left. We've been hoping she'd send word or come home, and she finally has. Looks like she sent us the best word we've had in years.

BUD. I knew she was trying to say I was the word that my momma sent.

MISS THOMAS. Wait here for one second, precious. *(She exits.)*

BUD. Miss Thomas was probably saying that as a excuse so she could blow her nose and cry.

(MISS THOMAS re-enters carrying a picture frame.)

MISS THOMAS. This has been on my dressing table for thirteen years. Now it belongs to you.

BUD. It was Momma. It'd been so long since I'd seen Momma smile that I wanted to laugh and cry at the same time.

MISS THOMAS *(moves the picture frame around)*. Do you see how her eyes are on you all the time? No matter which way you look at the picture, she's watching.

BUD. I can keep this?

MISS THOMAS. I feel like I've been holding on to it until the rightful owner came along. What took you so long, child? But Bud, we've got a problem I'm going to need your help with.

BUD. Uh-oh. I was going to have to fetch something for her.

MISS THOMAS. You can remember how bad you felt when you first knew she was gone?

BUD. Yes, ma'am. 'Cause it still feels the same.

MISS THOMAS. Well, you've had four years to try to heal that scar. Your grandfather and I just found out.

(Lights rise on HERMAN E. CALLOWAY.)

MISS THOMAS. The hurt is brand-new for us. There isn't a day that goes by that he doesn't think about her.

HERMAN E. CALLOWAY *(enters BUD's room)*. He loved her so much.

MISS THOMAS. Bud, sorry, sweetheart.

(She takes out a handkerchief and wipes her nose. CALLOWAY opens a little door. JIMMY enters. He crosses

to BUD's doorway and watches as CALLOWAY removes a heavy shoebox from behind the door.)

MISS THOMAS. Those stones that he picks up are for her. She must've been four or five years old; the band was getting ready to travel to Chicago and before we left he asked her—

HERMAN E. CALLOWAY. What she wanted him to bring back for her. He was thinking of a doll—

MISS THOMAS. or a dress or something, but she told him—

YOUNG MOMMA *(off stage)*. "A wock, Daddy, bring me back a wock from Chicago."

MISS THOMAS. So everywhere we went after that he'd have to get her a "wock." *(CALLOWAY pulls the Kentland rock out of his pocket. He pulls out a pen. His hands shake. He cannot write.)* He's got boxes of them upstairs,

HERMAN E. CALLOWAY. Eleven years worth. *(He sees JIMMY. He drops the rock in the shoebox, replaces it, and locks the door.)* Go get Grace.

MISS THOMAS. So, Bud, be patient with him. That ornery old man upstairs is very, very hurt right now and I just can't say where he's going to land after this news gets through blowing him around. So we're going to have to give him some time, we're going to—

(JIMMY crosses in; he has been crying.)

JIMMY. Grace, he wants you.

BUD. Herman E. Calloway was making everybody feel like they had the blues.

MISS THOMAS. You OK?
BUD. Yes, ma'am.
JIMMY. Mr. Jimmy went into the living room.

Scene 9

(BUD places the Broke-Back Bronco picture back in its envelope as the band comes crashing into the kitchen.)

BUD. Mr. C chose a good name for his house.
DOO-DOO-BUG. Hey, Sleepy LaBone, where's everyone at?
BUD. I didn't want to embarrass anyone by saying that all the grown folks were sitting all over the house sobbing their eyes out. They're around.
STEADY EDDIE. Well, it's you we wanted anyway. I told the fellas how hard you've been hitting that recorder, so we put a couple of nickels together—the Thug saw something at the pawnshop and we picked it up for you.

(BUD opens the suitcase. His gift is wrapped in newspaper. He unwraps it.)

BUD. I couldn't believe my eyes.

(STEADY EDDIE puts the horn together.)

STEADY EDDIE. It's an alto, Bud. I repadded, refelted and resprung it. The rest is up to you. Brasso. A man should polish his own horn. *(He pulls out a can.)*

BUD. I'll practice on this so much that I'll be just as good as you guys are in about three weeks!

(Laughter.)

STEADY EDDIE. Well, Mr. LaBone, I'll be back around seven. If you've got your ax polished up by then, I'll bring some sheet music along and we can get started Sound good?

BUD. Sounds great, Steady!

(STEADY EDDIE gives his neck strap to BUD and presents him with his horn. BUD puts it around his neck. He starts to bolt.)

DIRTY DEED. What, you ain't gonna blow us some notes, Mr. Three-Weeks-from-Now?

BUD. I'll let you hear me in three weeks when we're all on stage together.

DUG THE THUG. It's gonna take you at least ten years before you'll be able to even hold my drumsticks.

STEADY EDDIE. Yeah, and that's about nine years and ten months longer than you'll be with the band, Thug.

DUG THE THUG. Awww, man, you gotta let me know what you heard.

BUD. Thank you again. *(BUD grabs his belongings and breaks for his room. The band overlaps their versions of welcome.)*

DUG THE THUG. Nothing to it, little man.

DIRTY DEED. Now don't let that horn whip you, son.

DOO-DOO-BUG. Our pleasure, Sleepy.

STEADY EDDIE. Man, get outta here.

Scene 10

(BUD tears up the stairs and into his mother's old room. HERMAN E. CALLOWAY is revealed sitting at the dressing table, head in hands weeping.)

BUD. Woop, zoop, sloop…
HERMAN E. CALLOWAY. Mu-u-u-u-h… H-u-u-u-h…
BUD. Shucks. This was—

(Fanfare begins. ANNOUNCER makes to speak. BUD gestures for the music and the ANNOUNCER to halt.)

BUD. Rule Number 39. **The older you get, the worse something has to be to make you cry.** Crying's just like talking for a baby. When you got someone as old as Herman E. Calloway crying you know you're square in the middle of one of those boiling tragedies. He was acting like me being his grandson was the worst news anyone could ever give you in life.

(BUD drops the gary in. dot 6 rock in the pouch and grabs all of the flyers. He touches CALLOWAY. CALLOWAY sees BUD's face and jerks himself away.)

HERMAN E. CALLOWAY. Huh!… *(BUD gives him the flyers and the rocks.)* Herman E. Calloway's name was all over the flyers, and his writing was all over the rocks.
BUD. I figure they meant more to him than they did to me.
HERMAN E. CALLOWAY. I…I…how'd…look, Buddy… I…

BUD. It's Bud, sir, not Buddy. *(CALLOWAY puts his face back into his hands and exits as he falls apart.)* Man, it's a good thing the Thug wasn't around; no one would've wondered who the real Waterworks Willie was. *(He places his new picture on the dressing table. He takes a rock from his pocket and places it near the photo.)* I kept the rock that said Flint on it. My momma used to sleep in here when she was a little girl. *(He covers the bed with his old blanket. He takes his envelope and removes the picture of the Broke-Back Bronco photo. He tacks MOMMA and the bronco to the wall of horses.)* I put Momma right amongst all the ponies and horses she liked so much. This wasn't how I remembered Momma anyway.

(MOMMA walks in unnoticed by BUD. She adjusts the Broke-Back Bronco photo.)

MOMMA. It belonged.

BUD. I'd finally put Momma somewhere where she wanted to be. I didn't need those things with me all of the time. I couldn't think about Momma anymore if there were a hundred hours in every day and a thousand days in every week. All I have to do is remember her hand on my forehead.

MOMMA. Baby, are you sick? Have you got a temperature?

BUD. All I have to do is remember Momma letting me dry the dishes after she'd washed them.

MOMMA. No one in the world can dry a plate the way you can.

BUD. All I have to do is take two or three deep breaths and think of all the books she'd read to me at night.

MOMMA. And remember that no matter how long it takes I'll read until you go to sleep.

BUD. Deza Malone was right, I was carrying Momma inside me.

MOMMA. And there isn't anyone or anything that can take away from that or add to it either.

BUD *(picks up his ax)*. If after I got to ten I blew the horn and it sounded pretty good I knew I'd be playing along with the Dusky Devastators of the Depression in a week or two. If I didn't sound so good it meant I'd have to practice for a couple of months before I'd be good enough to get on stage with them. 1, 2, 3, 4, 5, 6, 7, 8, 9, 10! *(He blows.)* Shucks! Maybe I didn't puff my cheeks out right. *(He blows.)* It sounded great! I could tell those were the squeaks and squawks of one door closing and another one opening. Momma was looking right at me with that soft smile. (*He goes to his new picture of MOMMA sitting on the dressing table.)* I know it's stupid to smile back at a picture but I couldn't help myself. I know it's even stupider to talk to a picture, but I had to say, "Here we go again, Momma, only this time I can't wait!"

(He opens the can of Brasso. He begins to polish his horn. Lights out. END OF PLAY.)